Project Learning Tree®

Exploring Environmental Issues:

PLACES WE LIVE

Secondary Environmental Education Module

"Education is key—because people will not preserve what they don't understand. What they will not protect—they will lose."

—Ed McMahon, Urban Land Institute

"Whether working at the scale of the neighborhood, community, or region, the members of the American Planning Association know that young people bring critical insights and discerning minds to the process of envisioning and evaluating options for the future. The Places We Live curriculum can help prepare students to play a more active and informed role in that process while in school and for the rest of their lives as engaged citizens."

—Peter Hawley, American Planning Association

"When students are challenged to look at their communities critically and creatively, they develop an understanding of how the visual character of both the built and natural environment is an important component of the land use and development decisions that impact the growth and development of their communities—the forces that shape a community's character and sense of place."

—Sandra Ryack-Bell, The Dunn Foundation

"The students interacted well with the readings—they were challenged with the new information and utilized some of their prior knowledge of their community."

—New Mexico Educator

"The module contains powerful activities that encouraged my students to explore real-world problems and allowed them to work together to solve the problems."

—South Carolina Educator

"The background information is a strength of each PLT activity in this module. It is very helpful for a new teacher."

—Idaho Educator

Table of Contents

Acknowledgements

Support for this module was provided by:

The Dunn Foundation
Newport, RI

Ford Motor Company
Dearborn, MI

National Park Service
Washington, D.C.

American Planning
Association
Washington, D.C.

Urban Land Institute
Washington, D.C.

USDA Forest Service
Washington, D.C.

Project Learning Tree is a program of the American Forest Foundation.

American Forest Foundation

Tom Martin
President and CEO

Kenneth Stewart
Chair Board of Trustees

Project Learning Tree Staff

Kathy McGlauflin
Senior Vice President

Libby Backman
Program Coordinator

Rachel Bayer
Director of Education and
Network Partnerships

Vanessa Bullwinkle
Director of Communications

Haley Herbst
Program Coordinator

James McGirt
Manager of Education
Programs

Jennifer Pic
Manager of Instructional
Design and Technology

Jaclyn Stallard
Senior Manager of Education
Programs

Project Learning Tree
Operating Committee

Wanda Barrs
Due South Investments

Rob Beadel
Arkansas Forestry Association

Andrew Burnett
U.S. Fish & Wildlife Service

Laura Downey, Ph.D.
Committee Co-Chair, Kansas
Association for Conservation
and Environmental Education

Mary Ford
National Geographic Society

Nat Frazer, Ph.D.
Utah State University

Frank Gallagher, Ph.D.
Committee Co-Chair Rutgers
University

Mike Irvin
Oil City Elementary Magnet
School

Beth Marchand
Columbia Care

Michiko Martin
USDA Forest Service

Karen Ostlund, Ph.D.
University of Texas at Austin

Scott Richardson
Bureau of Land Management

Rafael Salgado
Cal-Wood Education Center

Susan Schultz
National Association of
Conservation Districts

Deborah Simmons, Ph.D.
National Project for
Excellence in Environmental
Education

Brenda Weiser, Ed.D.
University of
Houston-Clear Lake

Meta Williams, J.D.
United Negro College Fund

Project Directors –
Places We Live

Adena Messinger

Al Stenstrup

Places We Live Advisory
Committee

Alan R. Berkowitz
Institute of Ecosystem Studies
Millbrook, NY

David Carrier
American Planning
Association
Washington, DC

Dorothy Dunn
Cooper Hewitt,
National Design Museum
New York, NY

Naomi Friedman
Center for a New American
Dream
Takoma Park, MD

Frank Gallagher
New Jersey Division of Parks
and Forests
Trenton, NJ

Michelle Garland
Surface Transportation Policy
Project
Washington, DC

Peter Hawley
American Planning
Association
Washington, DC

Teri Heyer
USDA Forest Service
St. Paul, MN

Mike Hill
Shaw EcoVillage
Washington, DC

Ron M. Kagawa
Washington-Alexandria
Architecture
Alexandria, VA

Lorna Lange-Daggs
Joshua Tree National Park
Yucca Valley, CA

Linda Maxson
The Coastal Society
College of Ocean & Fishery
Sciences
Seattle, WA

Michael Pawlukiewicz
Urban Land Institute
Washington, DC

Bernadine Prince
American Farmland Trust
Washington, DC

Lester A. Ray
Apple Computer
Monmouth Junction, NJ

Sandra Ryack-Bell
The Dunn Foundation
Warwick, RI

Kris Wernstedt
Resources for the Future
Washington, DC

Writers and Editors

Cecelia Carver

Deron Davis

Naomi Friedman

Frank Gallagher

Jon Lepofsky

David Salvesen

Janna Six

Design and Copy Editors

202design

Publications Professionals LLC

Research Interns

Kristin Carlson

Aaron Hall

Writing Group
Liberty State Park,
New Jersey

John Benton
New Jersey Division of Parks
and Forests

Walter J. Bogan
University Heights Science Park

Mark Braza
U.S. Environmental Protection
Agency

Nikole Brugnoli
Conservation Consultants, Inc.

Heidi Busa
Marcellus High School

Jaimie Cloud
American Forum for Global
Education

Jeff England
World Wildlife Fund

Elizabeth Faircloth
Forest Resource Education
Center

Naomi Friedman
Center for a New American
Dream
Takoma Park, MD

Frank Gallagher
New Jersey Division of Parks
and Forests

John Graham
New York State Department
of Environmental Conservation

Joann Held
New Jersey Department of
Environmental Protection

Lou Iozzi
Rutgers University

Barry Jamason
New York State Deptartment
of Education

Elizabeth Johnson
Thomas Edison State College

Leib Kaminsky
National Association of
Service Conservation Corps

Amy Mallet
Forest Resource Education
Center

Gregory Mills
Harlem Environmental Impact
Project

Erik Mollenhauer
Education Information and
Resource Center

Paul Osmer
Glen Meadow Middle School

Tanya Oznowich
New Jersey Department of
Environmental Protection

Barbara Pietrucha
Neptune Middle School

Bernadine Prince
American Farmland Trust

Dave Reinecke
Maryland Department of
Natural Resources

Vicente Sanchez
USDA Forest Service

Dan Saunders
New Jersey Department of
Environmental Protection

Mike Strizki
New Jersey Department of
Transportation

Leah Yasenchak
City of Trenton

Writing Group
Rancho Santa Ana Botanic
Gardens, California

Bill Andrews
California Department of
Education

Kay Antunez
California Dept. of Forestry &
Fire Protection

Sonja Bickel
Teacher

Shawna Crocker
Colorado State Forest Service

Eric Edgerly
Castlemont High School

Richard Filson
Edison High School

Frank Gallagher
New Jersey Division of Parks
and Forests

Catania Galvan
Catania C. Galvan &
Associates

Jeff Hohensee
TreePeople

Leib Kaminsky
National Association of
Service Conservation Corps

Lorna Lange-Daggs
Joshua Tree National Park

Michael T. Mahoney
Forestry Consultant

Jean Nagy
Huntington Beach Tree
Society

Rudy A. Retamoza
GreenLink - USDA Forest
Service

Jack Shu
California State Parks

Janna Six
Environmental Education
Consultant

Darleen Stoner
California State University,
San Bernardino

Naomi White
Thomas Jefferson High School

Morgan Will
Friends of Trees

Writing Group
Chicago, Illinois

Aaron Becker

Goldeen Bell

Mary Burgess

Isabel Cernada

Mary Cummane

Irene DaMota

Jim Doyiakos

Theresa Dzoga-Borg

Connie Gaberik

Jack Giles

Samantha Godden-
Chmielowicz

Rita Greene

Patricia Guizzetti

Emiel Hamberlin

Jason Lauritgen

John Loehr

Nicole Malos

Marci Nettles

Christine Olsen

Martha Pedroza

Eleanor Prunckle

Eloise Roche

Jane Roll

Anne Marie Sherry

Bill Smith

Al Stenstrup

Julio Villegas

Dennis Zygadlo

Pilot Test Teachers

Karen Barker
Environmental Science,
Grade 12
Kinston, NC

Gale L. Bartley
Environmental Explorations,
Grades 11-12
Philomont, VA

Holly Borer
FFA, Grade 9
Logan, OH

Emily Bono
Freshman Seminar, Grade 9
Fort Wingate, NM

Pat Boshen
Integrated Science, Grade 9
Amberg, WI

Deborah Branson
Environmental Science,
Grades 10-12
Southern Pines, NC

Heidi Busa
Biomed, Grade 12
Skaneateles, NY

Sarah Jane Byars
Science, Grade 9
West Columbia, SC

Nikki Castleberry
Environmental Science,
Grades 10-12
Loganville, GA

Anna Gahl Cole
Environmental/Earth Science,
Grades 10-12
Albuquerque, NM

Joy Cowart
English, Grade 9
Hahira, GA

Jane Crosby
Earth/Environmental/
Atmospheric Science,
Grades 9-12
Statesville, NC

Lisa Durden
Applied Biology II,
Grades 10-12
Aiken, SC

Sarah A. Garcia
Environmental Science,
Grades 11-12
Atchison, KS

Jennifer Godrey
Science, Grade 6
Hubert, NC

Susan Goss
Integrated Science,
Grades 9-12
Cherry Hill, NJ

Jeri Gouch
Environmental Science,
Grade 9
Buies Creek, NC

Glenna Hoff
Horticulture Technology,
Grade 12
Marietta, OH

David Holder
Environmental Science,
Grade 11
Oklahoma City, OK

Leann Iacuone
Academic Biology I & Applied
Biology II, Grades 9-10
Laurens, SC

Gay L. Irwin
Honors Earth/Environmental
Science, Grades 11-12
Raleigh, NC

Kathryn Komoroski
AP Environmental Science,
Grades 11-12
Greenville, SC

Kali Kurdy
Student Leadership,
Grades 11-12
Boise, ID

Carla C. Little
Environmental Science,
Grade 10
Littleton, NC

Brian Matchett
Forestry Science, Grades 11-12
Spruce, MI

Joe Matteson
Biology, Grades 11-12
Espanola, NM

Carrie Newdigger
Advanced Biology,
Grades 11-12
Macksville, KS

Michele Nickels
Environmental Studies,
Grades 11-12
Minocqua, WI

John Niemoth
Physical Science, Grade 9
Waterloo, NE

Joel C. Rhymer
Ecology, Grades 11-12
Freedom, NH

Linda Rist
Natural Resources, Grade 9
Hartford, SD

Tom Saxton
Ecology, Grades 11-12
Appomattox, VA

Natalie Schaefer
Social Studies, Grades 7-12
Crescent City, CA

Sandra Schroerlucke
Environmental Science,
Grades 11-12
Louisville, KY

Tracy Shifflett
Ecology, Grades 11-12
Shenandoah, VA

Laura M. Struve
Environmental Education,
Grades 11-12
Amberg, WI

Natalie Tablan
Social Studies and
Environmental Studies,
Grades 9-12
Los Angeles, CA

Barb Thorson
Technology Coordinator,
Grades K-12
Statesville, NC

Teresa Tucker
Earth Science, Grade 9
Horton, MI

Adrian Walker
Zoology, Grade 9
Manhattan, KS

Jeanette S. Walker
Ecology, Grades 10-12
St. Petersburg, FL

Carol Widegren
Environmental Science,
Grades 10-12
Morton Grove, IL

Ginger Williams
Environmental Biology,
Grades 10-12
Croton, OH

Jimmy Woods
Biology I & Applied Biology II,
Grades 11-12
Florence, SC

Fred Zenk
Agriculture I, Grade 9
Webster, SD

Reviewers

Elaine Andrews
University of Wisconsin –
Environmental Resources
Center
Madison, WI

Kenneth Bateman
Argonne National Laboratory
Chicago, IL

Hooper Brooks
Surdna Foundation
New York, NY

Tim Brown
Center for Green Space
Design
Salt Lake City, UT

Roxanne Buchanan
Reynoldsburg, OH

Heidi Busa
Marcellus High School
Marcellus, NY

David Carrier
American Planning
Association
Washington, DC

Linda M. Casey
Marathon Ashland
Petroleum LLC
Findlay, OH

Joan Schumaker Chadde
Western U.P. Center
for Science, Math, &
Environmental Education
Michigan Technological
University
Houghton, MI

Cloe Chunn
Audubon Expedition Institute
Belfast, ME

Jennifer N. M. Coile
Community Development
Consultant
Hollister, CA

Sharon Katz Cooper
National Wildlife Federation
Reston, VA

Dolly Cummings
Camp Bayou Outdoor
Learning Center
Ruskin, FL

Chris Davis
Marin County Bicycle
Coalition
San Anselmo, CA

Thomas Dilley
USDA Forest Service
Evanston, IL

Susan Duncan
Washington Forest Protection
Association
Olympia, WA

Elizabeth Fedofsky
The Morton Arboretum
Lisle, IL

Lianne Fisman
M.I.T. Department of Urban
Studies and Planning
Boston, MA

Heather Francis
Tanglewood 4-H Camp and
Learning Center
Lincolnville, ME

Naomi Friedman
Center for a New American
Dream
Takoma Park, MD

Laura Gianakos
National Park Service
Lovell, Wyoming

Alice Cohen Goldstein
Forest Discovery Center
Pisgah Forest, NC

Rance Harmon
Penn State School of Forest
Resources Extension
University Park, PA

Susan Hayward
Stanton Bird Club
Lewiston, ME

Kate Helfrich
Freelance Writer
Dublin, OH

Heidi Hoover
UW – Stevens Point
Stevens Point, WI

Leslie C. Hyde
University of Maine
Cooperative Extension
Lincolnville, ME

Terry Ippolito
U.S. EPA Region 2
New York, NY

Alana Jensen
S. M. Stoller Corp.
Idaho Falls, ID

Patricia Julien
Mackay Whitsunday Natural
Resources Management
Group
Mackay, Queensland,
Australia

Susan Kain
Deer Flat National Wildlife
Refuge
Nampa, ID

Marti Kane
North Carolina State Parks
Raleigh, NC

Cecelia Carver King
Screech Owl Farm School
Moncure, NC

Gina Lagaly
Oklahoma Kids in
Environmental Education, Inc.
Yukon, OK

Cecilia Lammers, MP
Prince George's County
Planning
Upper Marlboro, MD

Lorna Sue Lange-Daggs
Joshua Tree National Park
29 Palms, CA

Christopher LeBlanc
Coronado National Forest
Tucson, AZ

Betsy A. Leonard
Independent Consultant
San Diego, CA

Mary J. Leou
New York University
New York, NY

Pat S. Lisoskie
Black Hills High School
Tumwater, WA

Gina Lockwood
Teacher
Boise, ID

Deycie Luke Dunlap
Eastern Idaho Visitors Center
Idaho Falls, ID

Edward Macie
USDA Forest Service
Atlanta, GA

Meg Maguire
Scenic America
Washington, DC

Lynn McCoy
Southwest Georgia Regional
Education Service Agency
Pelham, GA

Jeff D. Miller
Oak Leaf Consulting LLC
Greenville, OH

Hugh Morris
Rails-To-Trails Conservancy
Washington, DC

Ramona K. Mullahey
Center for Better
Communities
Honolulu, HI

Amy Avers-Nelson
City of Greensboro
Greensboro, NC

Michele Nickels
Nicolet Distance Education
Network
Rhinelander, WI

Lea Paddock
Peggy Notebaert Nature
Museum
Chicago, IL

Michael Pawlukiewicz
Urban Land Institute
Washington, DC

Curt Peters
University of Arizona
Tucson, AZ

Douglas R. Porter
Growth Management
Institute
Washington, DC

Gerard J. Ridzon, AICP
GEI Consultants, Inc.
Boston, MA

Linda Ries
USDA Forest Service
Ogden, UT

Anne Rilling
Smurfit-Stone Container
Corporation
Brewton, AL

Lidie Whittier Robbins
Northern Forest Center
White River Junction, VT

Kim Cleary Sadler
Middle Tennessee State
University
Murfreesboro, TN

Vicente Sanchez
USDA Forest Service
Hamden, CT

Lynn Schmitt-McQuitty
University of California
Cooperative Extension
Watsonville CA

Chris Schrager
Coronado National Forest
Tucson, AZ

Carolyn A. Smith
Pamlico-Tar River Foundation
Washington, NC

Cindy Smith-Walters
Middle Tennessee State
University
Murfreesboro, TN

Jim B. States
Wyoming PLT Steering
Committee
Saratoga, WY

Barb Thorson
Iredell-Statesville Schools
Statesville, NC

Tim Torma
U.S. Environmental Protection
Agency
Washington, DC

Brian M. Werner
Tiger Missing Link Foundation
Tyler, TX

Carol Widegren
Chicago Public Schools
Chicago, IL

Pamela Wridt
City University of New York
New York, NY

Linda Yunker
North Cook County Soil &
Water Conservation District
Carpentersville, IL

Cindy Zacks
Yucca Valley High School
Yucca Valley, CA

Elda D. Zounar
Idaho National Engineering
and Environmental
Laboratory
Idaho Falls, ID

**Project Learning Tree
Coordinators and
Workshops**

Project Learning Tree has a
network of state and provincial
partners and coordinators
who provide training workshops. For a current listing of
coordinators and information
on local workshops, please call
202-765-3641, or visit our
website, www.plt.org.

About Project Learning Tree

Project Learning Tree® (PLT) is widely recognized as one of the premier environmental education programs in the world. Through hands–on, interdisciplinary activities, PLT provides students with opportunities to investigate environmental issues and encourages them to make informed, responsible decisions.

PLT provides educators the tools they need to bring the environment into their classrooms and their students into the environment. Developed to meet state and national academic standards, PLT activities can be integrated into lesson plans for all grades and a multitude of subject areas.

PLT teaches students *how* to think, not *what* to think, about complex environmental issues. PLT activities make teaching and learning fun and connect children to nature. They engage students, improve student achievement, and grow 21st century skills that tomorrow's decision-makers need to succeed – including the ability to think critically and solve problems.

Each year in the U.S., over 25,000 educators attend PLT professional development workshops to learn how to integrate environmental education into their teaching. PLT programs are directed and implemented locally. This provides opportunities for enhancements to PLT's educational materials and professional development to specifically address the local environment, and meet educators' individual needs.

Project Learning Tree is a program of the American Forest Foundation. Since PLT began in 1976, PLT has trained more than 650,000 educators reaching an estimated 100 million students.

Quality Environmental Education

Environmental education is a process that increases the learner's awareness and knowledge about the environment and related issues. It helps to develop the necessary skills and expertise to address these issues, and fosters attitudes, motivations, and commitments to make informed decisions and take responsible action (UNESCO, Tbilisi Declaration, 1978). Environmental education enhances critical thinking, problem solving, and effective decision making skills, and it teaches individuals to weigh various sides of an issue to make informed and responsible

decisions. Environmental education does not advocate a particular viewpoint or course of action (Federal Register, Vol.62.No.163, 44860, August 22, 1997).

PLT's Mission

PLT advances environmental literacy and promotes stewardship through excellence in environmental education, professional development, and curriculum resources that use trees and forests as windows on the world.

PLT's Goals

- To develop students' awareness, appreciation, skills, and commitment to address environmental issues.
- To provide a framework for students to apply scientific processes and higher order thinking skills to resolve environmental problems.
- To help students acquire an appreciation and tolerance of diverse viewpoints on environmental issues and develop attitudes and actions based on analysis and evaluation of the available information.
- To encourage creativity, originality, and flexibility to resolve environmental problems and issues.
- To inspire and empower students to become responsible, productive, and participatory members of society.

How PLT Works

The PLT program consists of three essential elements:
- PreK–12 educational materials.
- Professional development for educators and other tailored trainings.
- Diverse and supportive professional network of educators and natural resource specialists.

PLT Materials: Development and Evaluation

PLT produces high-quality environmental education curriculum materials for early childhood through grade 12 to help educators teach about both the natural and built environments (see page 12). Topics include forests, wildlife, water, air, energy, waste, climate change, invasive species, biotechnology, biodiversity, and community planning, to name a few.

Educators can obtain PLT materials by attending a professional development workshop. Some materials are available for purchase directly from www.plt.org/store.

PLT materials are intended to supplement and support existing curricula. They are developed and designed to meet the needs of educators. For example, PLT lessons are aligned with academic standards and address current education trends. Hundreds of teachers, nonformal educators, and resource professionals help develop, review, field test, and independently evaluate all of PLT's curriculum materials. The process includes research, surveys, and writing workshops; revisions based on pilot testing and field testing; and formal assessment of impact on student learning by independent evaluators.

PLT materials have been reviewed formally (in a controlled environment) using both formative (review of content accuracy, checked for bias, pedagogy) and summative (pre-test, intervention lessons, post-test) evaluation. Independent evaluators conclude that PLT activities increase students' knowledge, reasoning, and academic skills.

PLT materials stay on the leading edge of quality environmental education through continuous review, revision, and evaluation.

The North American Association for Environmental Education points to PLT materials as examples of "model curriculum" in their Guidelines for Excellence.

Correlations to National and State Standards

PLT understands the importance of state-based standards. Visit PLT's website (www.plt.org) for a list of correlations between PLT activities and your state's academic standards.

PLT activities have been correlated to the Common Core State Standards for English Language Arts and Mathematics. The activities strongly support STEM (science, technology, engineering, and math) education and the Next Generation Science Standards' three dimensional approach. PLT remains on the pulse of new standards and is in the process of updating its materials to further support the new science standards. STEM Connections—a regular feature in PLT's e-newsletter, The Branch—offers educators ideas to expand PLT activities.

PLT's early childhood materials meet the student learning outcomes for Head Start and the National Association for the Education of Young Children. In addition, PLT connects with nonformal education programs. For example, PLT activities meet the requirements for Girl Scout Badges and Journeys for each level.

PLT Professional Development

PLT materials are available through professional development workshops. PLT was one of the first environmental education programs in the U.S. to establish professional development as part of its methodology. PLT workshops can be customized for specific grade levels, topic areas, and in-service trainings and teachers can earn continuing education credits. Though PLT, educators learn new teaching skills and become comfortable teaching outdoors.

Since PLT began in 1976, more than 650,000 educators have participated in a face-to-face PLT professional development workshop to learn how to connect kids to nature and engage students in hands-on, critical thinking activities—both outside and indoors. PLT also now offers professional development courses online. For more information, visit www.plt.org.

PLT Network

PLT's educational materials and customized professional development are delivered to educators via a vast network of international, national, state, and local partners. In each state, sponsoring organizations (state natural resource and education agencies, universities, and nonprofit organizations) employ PLT State Coordinators who carry out the PLT program in their state, and recruit and train facilitators to lead workshops. PLT also has agreements with sponsoring organizations in several other countries, such as Japan, Mexico, and Uruguay, and a partnership with the U.S. Peace Corps that trains their volunteers to use PLT activities with youth around the world.

From PLT staff, state coordinators, and workshop leaders; to classroom teachers and university faculty; to nature center staff, youth group leaders, and resource management professionals; to employees of state and federal government agencies, professional associations, and conservation education nonprofits; to business and industry; literally thousands of people work together to help students learn.

PLT Service Learning

Service learning is a powerful teaching tool that emphasizes critical thinking and problem solving, tackles challenges such as the environment and sustainability, and values people of all ages and abilities as having talents to offer. PLT encourages students to take personal responsibility for the environment and improve their school, home, and neighborhood based on what they learn in the classroom.

- The community action components of many PLT activities enrich learning by engaging students in meaningful service to their schools and communities through a process that is carefully linked to learning objectives.
- GreenSchools!, PLT's service-learning program, inspires students to apply their STEM and investigative skills to create greener and healthier schools – and save schools money.
- PLT offers GreenWorks! grants to help fund service-learning projects.

GreenSchools!

PLT's GreenSchools! program, in partnership with the U.S. Forest Service, engages students and teachers, school administrators and maintenance staff, and parents and community members in greening their school. Join more than 4,000 PLT GreenSchools nationwide and register your school at www.greenschools.org to access PLT's GreenSchools! Investigations.

GreenWorks!

PLT provides GreenWorks! grants to schools and youth organizations for service-learning projects that incorporate environmental education, link classroom learning with the real world, provide leadership opportunities for youth, and involve local community members.

Students "learn by doing" as they help design and lead projects to improve the environment in their local community. Elementary, middle, high school, and college students are planting trees, growing vegetable and native plant gardens, constructing outdoor classrooms, restoring streams and riparian habitats, creating hiking trails, starting recycling and composting programs, and saving energy, among other projects.

Since 1992, PLT has helped fund more than 1,200 GreenWorks! projects in communities across the U.S. Learn how to submit a proposal at www.greenworks.org. The annual deadline to apply for a PLT GreenWorks! grant is September 30th.

Pathways to GreenSchools!

- Teachers and student leaders form a Green Team, in which teachers and administrators are the facilitators, and students are the driving force.

- Five PLT GreenSchools! Investigations provide a blueprint for individual students or whole classes to examine their school's energy use, waste and recycling, water consumption, school site, and environmental quality (such as indoor air quality, school transportation, and use of chemicals) — and establish benchmarks.

- Using the results of their investigations, students select, design, and implement one or more action projects, and measure their impacts. PLT offers GreenWorks! grants to support these projects.

- Importantly, it's students who lead the way. Students learn they can make a difference in the world as they are empowered to make changes and take ownership of the projects they lead to reduce their school's environmental footprint.

PLT Resources and Support

The PLT website (www.plt.org) provides a wealth of information regarding all of PLT's programs. The site includes information on correlations to your state's curriculum standards, enhancements to activities, resources that support them (including copyright-free student pages), GreenSchools! and GreenWorks! grants, new materials, and initiatives like PLT's online professional development.

The Branch

PLT's quarterly e-newsletter, The Branch, provides news of new PLT materials, recommendations for environmental education resources, grant opportunities, and articles by educators that focus on practical teaching tips and proven ways to use PLT materials with students in the classroom and outdoors. Go to the PLT website to sign up to receive it. You can also follow PLT's Blog for more frequent and timely news and resources, and join us on social media.

Your PLT State Coordinator

Contact your PLT State Coordinator for local resources and assistance, including information about in-person professional development workshops in your area and becoming a workshop facilitator. Visit www.plt.org for your PLT State Coordinator's contact information.

Environmental Experiences for Early Childhood

Designed for educators who work with children ages 3 to 6, over 130 hands-on experiences engage young children in outdoor exploration and play. Activities integrate investigations of nature with art, literature, math, music, and movement. An accompanying music CD encourages children to sing, dance, and move. *Learning*® magazine 2011 Teachers' Choice℠ Award winner.

PreK–8 Environmental Education Activity Guide

PLT's flagship curriculum resource contains 96 multi-disciplinary activities each tailored to specific grade levels and correlated to state and national academic standards. Hands-on activities develop students' STEM, critical-thinking, problem-solving, and other 21st century skills. Each activity includes background and science content for teachers; student assessment tools; literature connections; technology extensions; cooperative learning; and differentiated instruction.

Energy & Society Kit

Designed for best use with grades 4-8, PLT's *Energy & Society* kit helps students investigate environmental issues related to energy's role in society. The kit includes an activity guide, an award-winning *Energy & Me* music CD and dance DVD, and two sets of posters.

PLT's Secondary Modules

For high school educators PLT's secondary modules challenge students to explore in depth the many facets of an issue – illustrating the complexity of real life environmental decisions. Hands-on classroom studies, research, and collaborative field investigations provide students opportunities to debate issues and engage with experts.

PLT's secondary modules include: Focus on Forests; Forests of the World; Places We Live; Municipal Solid Waste; Biodiversity; Focus on Risk; and Biotechnology.

PLT's GreenSchools! Investigations

At the heart of the PLT GreenSchools! program are five hands-on, student-driven investigations that focus on STEM education: Energy, Water, School Site, Waste and Recycling, and Environmental Quality. To access the materials, register your school at www.greenschools.org and download or order a print copy. The investigations provide directions for student Green Teams, things to measure and observe, worksheets to fill out, guidance on how to combine data into a school-wide analysis, and tips for students to create and implement action plans.

Nature Activities for Families

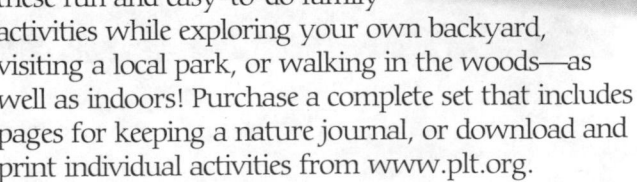

Encouraging children to spend time outside and play in nature can improve their creativity and imagination, classroom performance, and academic achievement, as well as their overall health and fitness. Try these fun and easy-to-do family activities while exploring your own backyard, visiting a local park, or walking in the woods—as well as indoors! Purchase a complete set that includes pages for keeping a nature journal, or download and print individual activities from www.plt.org.

Notes

_____

_____

_____

_____

_____

_____

_____

_____

_____

_____

_____

_____

_____

_____

_____

_____

_____

_____

_____

Larger than any fish I had ever seen, it was chasing baitfish in a small tidal creek. For a large fish, it was very fast. Realizing that the tide was falling, I built a coffer dam at the mouth of the creek. Within half an hour, most of the water had drained and I chased the fish onto the shore. I was amazed at how clumsy the fish moved once it was out of the water. Still, it would be a very successful hunt. All I had to do was kill and clean this trophy so that I could bring it home for dinner. I was sure that my parents would be proud.

I found a large rock. Wanting a quick kill, I studied the fish for a long time. As I stared, the fish began to look back at me. I didn't know what it was thinking, but I knew it was thinking. The rock in my hand became increasingly heavy. Looking again at the fish, I decided that it probably didn't taste very good anyway. I destroyed the dam and pushed the fish back into the water. That fish was my first of what developed into a long line of "You should have seen the one that got away" stories.

The tidal creek where I played is gone—now part of Route 440, a highway that allows for high-speed connections between Bayonne and Jersey City. However, for me, the image is still clear and very much a part of who I am.

—Frank Gallagher, New Jersey

Think back to your childhood. Where did you play? How did you get around? What are your most vivid memories of those places? Can you still sense the smells, sights, and sounds? Why do you think those memories have remained? We all have strong experiences of places; they originate from the city sidewalks, the suburban yards, and the back 40 acres of the farm. They shape who we are and whom we will become. "If you don't know where you are," says Wendell Berry, "you don't know who you are."[1] An ecological, social, cultural, and historical identity all contribute to one's *sense of place*.

Why Study the Places We Live?

Whether you live in a city, suburb, small town, or rural countryside, your community is always changing. The population may be growing or declining, buildings may be torn down and new ones constructed, and new roads may be planned or a new bus line added. If we look at the country as a whole, in 1970, the U.S. population was approximately 205 million; in 2004, it surpassed 293 million; and by 2040, it is expected to reach 391 million.[2] (See Figure 1.) All of those people will need *places* to live, work, and play. Growth is inevitable, and how your community chooses to grow can profoundly affect *environmental quality*, *public health*, *community character*, *sense of place*, and *quality of life*.

Figure 1 U.S. Population Growth

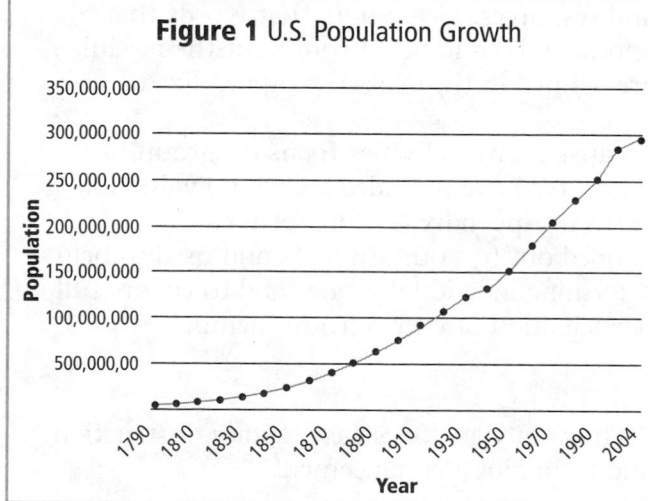

Year	Population	Year	Population	Year	Population
1790	3,929,214	1880	50,189,209	1970	205,052,000
1800	5,308,483	1890	62,979,766	1980	227,726,000
1810	7,239,881	1900	76,212,168	1990	250,132,000
1820	9,638,453	1910	92,228,496	2000	282,434,000
1830	12,866,020	1920	106,021,537	2004	293,846,745
1840	17,069,453	1930	123,202,624	2010	308,936,000
1850	23,191,876	1940	132,164,569	2020	335,805,000
1860	31,443,321	1950	151,325,798	2030	363,584,000
1870	39,818,449	1960	179,323,175	2040	391,946,000

Source: U.S. Census Bureau, 2004 (E)

The places in which we live are changing in many ways, including resource availability, appearance, function, and size. Furthermore, the changes are occurring more rapidly than ever before. What are the environmental, social, and economic effects of those changes? As an area grows or declines, how can citizens work together to manage the changing needs of land development, transportation, public services, and protection of natural and cultural resources? By beginning our exploration in our own backyards, we can connect with our surroundings and learn how to work as a community to protect the environmental, social, and economic integrity of the places in which we live.

Purpose of the Module

The purpose of this module is to provide opportunities for community investigations that focus on environmental, social, and economic issues and to help students and other community members develop and strengthen their sense of place. The goals of the module are:

- To teach students the skills and knowledge to be active participants in shaping their community
- To connect students to the places they live (or to highlight that connection) so they will care about and influence the decisions being made about those places
- To give students an awareness of the environmental, social, and economic issues connected to community growth and change
- To help students understand that their choices affect the environment and the quality of life in communities near and far

How to Use the Module

This module is designed for grades 9–12 and can easily be adapted for formal and nonformal settings, as well as for adult or middle school audiences. As an interdisciplinary supplemental curriculum, the activities address concepts in social studies, geography, civics, language arts, health, and science. The activities are correlated to national and state education standards in social studies and science and can be used as a unit of study or as standalone lessons to complement any curriculum.

As you look through the module, you will note that it has three major sections: (1) Background Information for Educators, (2) a series of inquiry-based Activities, and (3) Appendices.

The Background Information for Educators provides a general overview of the topics covered and will help you lead the activities in the module. Each activity also includes a background section with additional information for educators on each specific topic. Endnotes are found at the end of the Background section of each activity. Letters following author and date citations refer to sections in the bibliography (Appendix B) where the reader can find full data about the sources cited.

The activities are designed to engage your students in meaningful inquiry and to move them from awareness, to knowledge, to challenge or consensus, and finally to action. Each activity uses the constructivist philosophy of teaching to build on the knowledge your students already have and to help them develop useful problem-solving and decision-making skills. The activities also provide opportunities for your students to get involved in community action projects and service learning.

The appendices provide additional information and resources. Please note that words that appear in bold italics throughout the module are defined in the Glossary, Appendix A.

Because many activities focus on group work, we have provided a Group Evaluation Form in Appendix G. This form can be handed out to your students and used to help determine individual grades and to ensure full participation of every group member.

Activities

Each activity includes case studies, instruction, and technology enhancements.

Case Studies

The case studies feature communities across the country and were selected to illustrate what real people are doing to address community environmental issues. Some of the case studies presented are integral to the activity, while others are intended as enhancements that can help you in teaching the activity and can help your students in gaining a deeper understanding of the issue. If you find that the case studies in the module do not suit your needs, please visit the case study database on the PLT website at www.plt.org for more examples.

Instruction

The activities in the module are designed to provide the educator with a framework for conducting community investigations. The first activity in the module sets the stage for helping learners identify and develop a sense of place within their communities. The remaining activities provide opportunities for students to conduct in-depth community investigations by building on their knowledge, challenging what they learn, and encouraging positive action to improve their communities. Each activity reinforces the concept of sense of place, always connecting the learners to their environment and their place within it.

For quick reference, each activity includes a sidebar that notes the related subjects, objectives, suggested time considerations, materials, skills, and connection to the PLT

Conceptual Framework (see Appendix J). Some of the longer activities are broken down into parts (e.g., Part A, Part B) to help determine how longer activities might be conducted in smaller steps. At the end of each activity, you can find suggestions for authentic assessment opportunities, as well as ways to enrich the lessons.

Technology Enhancements

Although it is not necessary to use computers to teach the activities, we have provided a number of technology enhancements that will enrich the learning experience for both students and teachers, including these:

- Web addresses for links to helpful images, graphs, and other resources. You can gain quick access by going to a Quick Links page on the PLT website at www.plt.org to find all the links in one place.
- Suggestions for using software programs that complement the lesson
- Additional case studies that you can use with the activities and that are available through the PLT website at www.plt.org
- Resource database that is correlated to the different sections and that is made available through the PLT website at www.plt.org

Service-Learning Opportunities through PLT's GreenWorks! Program

Service learning is a teaching method that blends service activities with the academic curriculum and addresses real community needs. This module includes suggestions for service-learning projects to help students learn through active engagement (see the Enrichment sections of the activities.)

GreenWorks! is Project Learning Tree's service-learning program. It provides educators with grants to help fund student-led environmental action projects that link classroom learning and the real world. Educators, students, and community members are encouraged to partner together to complete environmental improvement projects in their neighborhood. These GreenWorks! projects make a difference in how young people examine their environment and understand their relationship to the environment, and help them develop a sense of responsibility toward their community.

GreenWorks! projects are fun, benefit the community, and—perhaps most importantly—reinforce the learning that takes place in the classroom. Visit www.plt.org for more information and apply for a PLT GreenWorks! grant. PLT also has a free online guidebook, *GreenWorks! Connecting Community Action and Service-Learning*, with practical pointers to help you get started.

Activity Overviews

Activity 1: Personal Places
Students investigate and report on their connection with a special place and with their greater community.

Activity 2: Community Character
Students explore community character and investigate ways that communities, including their own, are responding to growth and development pressures.

Activity 3: Mapping Your Community Through Time
Student teams investigate the social, cultural, economic, aesthetic, and environmental components of their community to create map overlays and reports describing the development of their community through time.

Activity 4: Neighborhood Design
Students explore the current layout of their neighborhoods, critically evaluate a variety of development options, and formulate ideas for guiding further growth in their communities.

Activity 5: Green Space
Students investigate green infrastructure and native plant communities at the neighborhood, community, and regional scales. They also explore the dual needs to accommodate population growth and to protect green space and native plant communities.

Activity 6: A Vision for the Future
Student teams develop and present a vision for the future of an area in their community.

Activity 7: Far-Reaching Decisions
Students develop graphic organizers and creative presentations to illustrate how individual decisions can impact the local environment, as well as distant communities. They also measure their own ecological footprint.

Activity 8: Regional Community Issues: The Ogallala Aquifer
Students investigate a regional issue as they adopt the roles of shareholders and debate solutions to the depletion of North America's largest aquifer.

Human life swings between two poles: movement and settlement.

—Lewis Mumford (A)

From the beginning of human habitation, settlement patterns have been determined by the availability of basic resources—water, food, and shelter. Settlements have been defined by architectural artifacts or the remnants of civilization, such as religious sanctuaries, meeting places, centers of commerce, and cemeteries.[3] From the earliest settlements through the rise and fall of ancient Rome, and from the European colonization of New England through today, humans have sought to create **places** to live—villages, towns, cities, and suburbs—and to transform those places into communities.

How Is Land Use Changing in the United States?

Urban Growth

Toward the end of the 19th century, the majority of the population in the United States was still living in rural areas; even still, U.S. cities had grown by 15 million people. (See Figure 2.) Many of the new **urban** dwellers were either immigrants or former rural residents in search of economic opportunity and the promise of a better life. In addition, the industrialization of food production—characterized by an increase in mechanized power and chemical use—had changed the nature of agriculture from the small farm to factory farms.[4] By 1920, the urban and suburban population outnumbered the rural population and has retained that majority ever since, accounting for approximately 80 percent of the U.S. population in 2000.[5]

From 1920 until the mid-1960s, large industrial cities were the nation's core for population and employment, forming the economic centers where most Americans lived and worked. Since the 1960s, however, the situation has changed markedly. Today, more people live and work in suburbs than in cities.[6]

Figure 2 U.S. Urban vs. Rural Population, 1800–2000

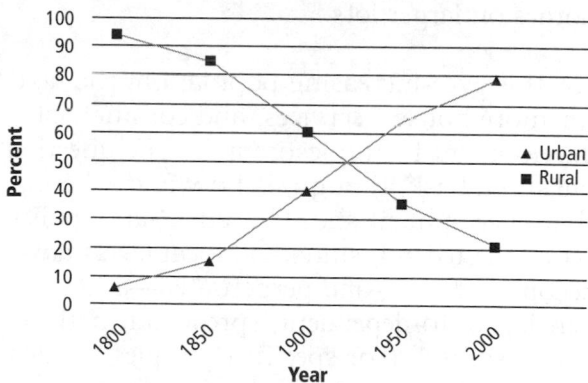

Note: An area is considered "urban" if it has more than 2,500 people.
Source: U.S. Census Bureau, 2000 (E).

The major cause of changes in **land use** in the United States is development in and around urban areas; since the 1970s, urban area in the United States has more than doubled.[7] Most of the growth is occurring at the edges of cities, but rural areas are growing too.[8] In much of America, our suburbs and cities have merged into what is generally referred to as **metropolitan** areas. For links to charts on population growth in U.S. cities, visit www.prb.org.

What Accounts for the Changes in Land Use?

One important force driving current urbanization is population growth (from immigration, fertility rates, and improvements in medical care). As more people move into an area, the need for new housing rises. As houses are planned for development, other development is planned as well, including schools, roads, sewers, water supplies, energy supplies, waste management, and recreational areas.[9] Tied closely to this cycle are the social and economic conditions of the area. For example, employment opportunities and economic conditions help to dictate the movement of people among cities, suburbs, and farms, as well as the demand for new housing or movement of families into larger homes on larger lots.[10]

For this ever-increasing population, the need for more houses, services, and commercial development is unquestionable. The question we should ask, though, is how and where that development should occur. Many policies set at the federal, state, and local levels have accommodated—and perpetuated—a low-density, auto-dependent, spread-out pattern of urban sprawl. (For specific examples of such policies, please see Appendix D.) Some more recent policies, however, have attempted to limit **sprawl**, including Portland, Oregon's, **urban growth boundary**.

Another factor influencing land use is personal choice. Each person in the United States uses, on average, more land today than in the past. A study conducted by the Brookings Institution indicated that between 1982 and 1997, the amount of land consumed for urban development increased by 47 percent while the nation's population during that time grew by only 17 percent.[11] Personal choice also influences the shopping, recreational, and social infrastructure that is developed in communities.

Trends in Development Patterns

Sprawling, spread-out development describes the U.S. style of growth since the 1950s. Home loan programs established through the

Federal Housing Administration (FHA) and the GI Bill of Rights encouraged many prospective homeowners to move to communities on the urban fringe. Those programs also enabled veterans and young families to purchase affordable single-family homes in new suburban communities. FHA's policies favored single-family housing (versus multifamily units), new construction (versus rehabilitation of existing structures), and all-white neighborhoods (versus racially diverse communities). In response to the projected demand for new housing, the government established finance programs that encouraged developers to build cookie-cutter developments on large tracts of land.[12] As people moved out, cities suffered neglect and decay, further driving middle-class residents into the suburbs; as a result, outlying areas experienced explosive growth.[13]

Changing transportation options have been instrumental in influencing growth and land use patterns over the years. In the mid-19th century, most people walked to work. In the late 19th and early 20th centuries, railroads and streetcars fostered suburban spread, largely along linear paths. Over the past 50 years, the mobility offered by individuals owning cars effectively opened up vast tracts of land to development.

Federal policy has also played a significant role. In 1956, Congress enacted the Interstate Highway Act, which called for the construction of 41,000 miles of expressways (see Appendix

D). It was one of the largest public works projects ever undertaken in this country. In short order, new multilane highways encircled cities, sliced through inner-city neighborhoods, and facilitated the exodus of businesses and residents to the suburbs, which continues to this day, contributing to economic opportunities, more **affordable housing** options, and sprawling land use.

Today, with the completion of the interstate highway system, some funds from the federal gasoline tax have been shifted to support transportation alternatives; mass transit, bicycle, and pedestrian projects have been made possible by the 1991 Intermodal Surface Transportation Enhancement Act (for more on this act, please see Appendix D).

To service the new suburban development, states and communities built new roads, schools, sewage systems, drinking water facilities, and power plants. Local governments raised taxes to pay for the new services and infrastructure. Residents became increasingly dependent on the automobile to travel to work and to secure even the most basic services or goods. The inner suburbs began to suffer from the same problems that cities had experienced—traffic congestion, air and water pollution, and crime—and more affluent residents abandoned their homes in search of newer neighborhoods farther and farther out. The nation experienced a rapid loss of farmland, **green space**, and

scenic beauty that was paved over to accommodate the new communities. Also lost was a discernable center where commerce and services were concentrated and a community's character could be identified.

Another significant contributor to the trend of spread-out development is conventional local **zoning** codes. Zoning designates the size and width of lots, the dimensions or "bulk" of buildings, special historic districts, and flood plain areas. Local governments typically divide the community into zoning districts that separate different land uses, such as residential, commercial, industrial, or no development at all. The intention of separating the uses is to maintain land values and to protect public and private interests. For example, prohibiting polluting industries from locating near residential areas is intended to protect residents from injury and to preserve the value of their homes.

Together, the forces—auto transportation, federal policy, and conventional zoning—helped create the widely dispersed patterns of development that now characterize much of the United States. Compared to the rest of the world, our metropolitan regions are far less compact. For example, metropolitan areas in Europe average three to four times the density of typical U.S. urban areas. U.S. cities are also the world's least centralized in terms of employment.[14] For models of land use in the United States, please visit http://landcover-modeling.cr.usgs.gov/index.php.

Reactions to Sprawl

People have different reactions to current growth patterns in the United States. Some argue that the development trends are a result of market demand and are enabling fulfillment of the dream to own a home and some land in the suburbs because the dream is more affordable. In addition, because the United States has a long-standing tradition of private land ownership, private land owners have great latitude in determining how to use their land, and attempts to curb sprawl may be seen as conflicting with private property rights.

Others argue that we need a fundamental shift in the way we think about our housing and transportation wants and needs because current growth patterns are proving to be unsustainable. Overall, antisprawl sentiment is on the rise.[15] According to a poll conducted in 2000 by Smart Growth America, which is a coalition of more than 60 public interest groups, more than three-quarters of those surveyed said that they favored "giving priority to improving services, such as schools, roads, affordable housing, and public transportation in existing communities rather than encouraging new housing and commercial development and new highways in the countryside."[16]

Return to the Cities?

Today, **planners**, **designers**, community groups, and local and state government officials seek ways to draw people back into town centers and urban hubs. They are designing communities to protect **green infrastructure** and open space, to reduce air and water pollution, to expand housing and transportation choices, and to improve residents' quality of life.

Some cities have experienced a rebirth in recent years. Many U.S. cities continue to possess unique features (such as diversity, mass transit, and mixed-use areas) that, in combination with efforts to improve the quality of life, have helped make those cities more competitive with suburbs. Together with renewed immigration, the improvements have helped foster some of the first population increases in cities in several decades. At the same time, rapid growth and development continue in the nation's outer suburbs.[17] The relative balance of people who seek the suburbs or stay in cities remains to be seen.

Environmental Impacts

Although a survey of our nation's land resources might reveal an abundance of open space, in truth most U.S. residents live in or near cities. Populations in urban and suburban areas place extreme pressure on land resources in those areas. The ways in which we build and develop our communities and use and protect the land have significant environmental effects. A few examples are highlighted next. Although we have formidable challenges ahead in terms of managing development while simultaneously protecting our environment, we have made significant steps in that direction. Furthermore, as public awareness and knowledge of such issues grow, we are in a better position as a society and as individuals to make informed decisions and to seek solutions that benefit both humans and the environment.

Coastal Areas

Only 17 percent of the acreage that makes up the lower 48 states is coastal (defined as a band stretching 50 miles inland from the ocean, as well as the areas bordering the Great Lakes). Since the 1960s, this zone has been home to more than 50 percent of the U.S. population. The number of people living in the coastal zone and current trends in land use, transportation, and recreation add up to extreme environmental pressure on coastal resources. For tables and a map of coastal population and development figures, go to http://oceanservice.noaa.gov/programs/mb/supp_cstl_population.html.

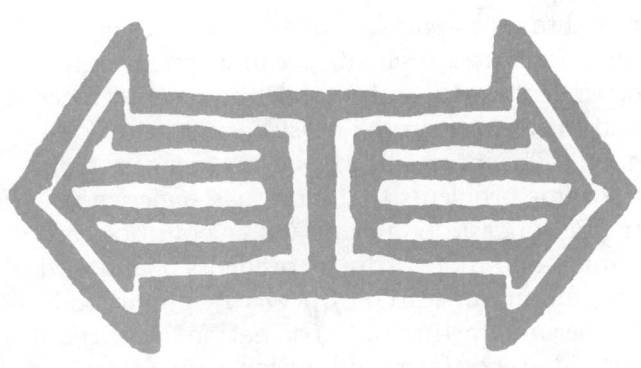

Over a 15-year period (between 1982 and 1997), noncoastal areas were developed at a rate of 0.08 percent per year, while coastal areas were developed at a rate of 0.25 percent per year. If this trend continues, more than one-fourth of the U.S. coastal area will be developed by 2025. Those numbers are significant from the perspective of environmental protection (in particular **watershed** protection) because increases in development translate into increases in impervious surfaces such as roads and parking lots. And, according to a number of studies over the past decade, when the impervious land area of a watershed reaches more than 10 percent, the rivers and streams within that watershed become seriously degraded. Examples of degradation include the following:

- Increased erosion and sedimentation of streams, which results in decreased habitat quality;
- Increased water temperatures affecting the health and survival of aquatic organisms; and
- Increased pollutants entering the water (such as nitrogen, hydrocarbons, salt, sediment, and trace metals) from urban runoff, which affects plants and animals that live in those waters.[18]

What measures can help safeguard our coastal areas? At the regional level, some strategies involve newly zoning areas to establish separate places for development and protection, evaluating planned investments in new-growth infrastructure (e.g., roads, sewers, waste management) within the context of environmental impacts, assessing agricultural practices, and creating a land conservation program for purchasing development rights to sensitive or strategic areas so that the areas will not be used. At the neighborhood level, increasing housing density (versus using undeveloped land for housing) can help protect open space from becoming impervious and can potentially reduce air and water pollution from transportation sources.[19] In addition, new technology to treat stormwater runoff on a microscale for both quantity and quality should be emphasized in coastal communities to recharge groundwater sources and to protect receiving streams and rivers.

Air Quality

Land use patterns also have a direct effect on traffic and, consequently, air quality. Between 1977 and 2001, vehicle miles traveled in the United States increased by more than 60 percent.[20] According to the U.S. Department of Transportation, land use factors such as sprawling development were responsible for more than 60 percent of the growth in automobile travel.[21] Automobiles and other mobile sources (such as trucks) are widely recognized as significant sources of air pollution. Worldwide, vehicle exhaust is often the dominant ingredient in urban air pollution, which takes at least three million lives each year.[22] Air pollution can be reduced, though, if we purchase efficient, low-emission cars, drive less, carpool, and walk or bicycle for short trips. People can also insist on regulations and incentives that reduce pollutants emitted by factories and other fuel-burning industries such as power plants. Finally, people can support growth that stresses **compact** and **transit-oriented development** and **mass transit** systems in our communities.

Agricultural Lands

According to the U.S. Department of Agriculture, about 68 percent of the total land area in the United States consists of farmland (including cropland, pastureland, rangeland, and forestland). However, as of 1997, only about 25 percent of that farmland was classified as **prime farmland**.[23] Some of the fastest growth in the country is occurring beyond the areas now defined as metropolitan, in communities 60 to 70 miles from metropolitan beltways that are still rural. According to the American Farmland Trust, between 1982 and 1992 the United States lost an average of 400,000 acres per year of prime farmland to urban and suburban development. During that same period, the country lost an additional 26,600 acres of farmland that had been used for growing rare and specialty crops.[24]

Unfortunately, much of the land best suited for productive farming—often in flat river valleys and on well-drained soils—is also well suited for development. According to the American Farmland Trust, California's Central Valley is the nation's most threatened agricultural region, which is beleaguered by particularly high development rates. The valley is also one of the nation's most productive agricultural regions, supporting a massive $13.3 billion farming industry and producing a significant amount of the nation's fruit and vegetables.[25] Although the current loss of farmland does not appear to be an immediate threat to the nation's overall food supply, it may be a serious local issue and one that affects particular segments of the food market, as well as jobs and revenue. Loss of farmland around expanding metropolitan areas also diminishes scenic landscapes and open space available to nearby metropolitan residents.[26]

Disappearing Green Space

Agricultural land is not the only open space at risk. We're also losing woodlands, wildlands, and wetlands. Collectively, most Americans live on a small percentage of our country's land surface—our metropolitan areas. In fact, only about 5 percent of the total U.S. land area is considered developed. From the perspective of many metropolitan residents, the most precious green space is the green space that remains within their neighborhoods. Yet it is this very green space that is most threatened, given our current development patterns.[27]

Governments have long recognized the need to preserve open spaces because of their importance in producing public goods and services, including food, fiber, recreation, and natural hazard mitigation. They have also recognized the important geographical and biological features that they possess. New impetus for open space preservation has come from efforts to counteract sprawl and to preserve the natural beauty and amenities that make a community a desirable place to live. To protect open space, states and

municipalities have used a number of strategies, including the following:

- Purchasing land
- Establishing **conservation easements** that restrict land uses
- Creating **land trusts** and special taxation rates
- Transferring or purchasing development rights
- Setting aside portions of large developments as open space
- Revising zoning and tax laws to reduce development incentives
- Educating private land owners
- Using conservation design strategies that allow development to coexist with green space protection

The preservation of green space—locally, regionally, nationally, and globally—is increasingly important, given our influence on the land. Although only a small portion of the Earth's surface may be considered "developed," our influence on the landscape is remarkable. To investigate our impact on planet Earth, a team of scientists from the Wildlife Conservation Society and Columbia University's Center for International Earth Science Information Network created a Human Footprint map.[28] The map, designed to illustrate the extent of human activities and to identify opportunities for conservation, shows that human beings affect 83 percent of the Earth's land surface.[29] To view the map, visit http://earthobservatory.nasa.gov/Features/footprint.

Biodiversity

Humans are not the only ones to benefit from open space conservation. As we develop our land, we lose wildlife habitat. Although some species can tolerate—or even thrive—in disturbed habitats, many other species are lost. As we develop land, we often fragment and degrade terrestrial and aquatic ecosystems. Many rare and specialized species require large, contiguous, undisturbed open spaces to survive, and they become threatened by barriers that reduce or fragment their habitats.[30] Development can disrupt breeding and migration patterns, thereby isolating populations in small habitat remnants.

In an assessment of roughly 20,000 plant and animal species native to the United States, The Nature Conservancy (TNC) reports that one-third are "of conservation concern" or are believed to be extinct, threatened, or vulnerable. According to TNC, "The leading cause of imperilment is habitat degradation and destruction. While outright destruction is usually quite obvious, alteration and degradation of sensitive habitats can be subtle, often occurring over long periods of time and escaping notice."[31]

As we pave over or fill wetlands, we lose some of the most biologically rich ecosystems on Earth. Wetland habitats have been hit hard; in total, human activity has taken more than 53 percent of the 221 million acres of wetlands once found in the lower 48 states. About one-half of the animals and one-third of the plant species listed as endangered or threatened depend on wetlands.[32] According to the U.S. Fish and Wildlife Service, suburban sprawl is the leading cause of wetland loss.[33]

Societal Impacts

Growth and the ways we choose to develop our communities have social and environmental consequences. Social and environmental issues are deeply interconnected, thus blurring the distinction between them. Following are several examples of primarily social consequences and challenges that we face because of development pressures.

Traffic

One of the most common complaints about sprawl is the resulting traffic congestion. More than any other factor, excessive traffic (both perceived and real) causes citizens to raise concern about growth in suburbia. In most U.S. cities, the traffic is worse in the suburbs than in downtown areas. The amount of time motorists in urban areas spend in traffic has increased to about 50 hours a year, compared to 34 hours a year in 1990.[34] What causes the traffic? People driving out of convenience, necessity, and pleasure cause it. The average household currently generates 13 car trips per day because, in most neighborhoods, homes, schools, workplaces, and stores are spread out and because safe and practical bicycle or walking routes, as well as convenient mass transit systems, are lacking. But another key factor lies in how suburbs are organized. Instead of a traditional neighborhood with numerous through streets and options to travel from point A to point B, the modern suburb has collector roads that often funnel traffic onto one main road. In case of traffic or an accident, other options are limited.[35]

Loss of Community Character

Many North American cities from the late 1800s and the early or mid 1900s were characterized by distinct neighborhoods that reflected the ethnic heritages of their immigrant populations. Such a multiethnic society still characterizes many cities today.[36] The same, however, cannot be said for the suburbs. Pull off any interstate highway interchange, and you enter a landscape cluttered with the same national chains of gas stations, restaurants, and inexpensive motels. You could be anywhere. Gone are the local influences in architecture, cuisine, hospitality, and entertainment.

Although not all suburbs are void of character, the sameness of our suburban landscape diminishes a sense of place. Those features that make a village, town, or city unique and that foster a sense of place are giving way to a creeping homogenization that dilutes the influences of local culture, style, and traditions.

Two of the most important steps for preserving a community's ecological integrity and visual and cultural character are (1) evaluating the positive and negative attributes of the community and (2) developing a common vision among residents, landowners, elected officials, public land managers, and other stakeholders about what they value in the community and what they want for the future. That vision can be a powerful tool, galvanizing the community to take action and improve the place in which they live.

Quality of Life Issues

All across the country—in growing urban centers, small towns, and rural communities—people are talking about quality of life. Because so many people use the term "quality of life" in so many ways, the term remains loosely defined. Yet, even with this ambiguity, quality of life is a guiding force in many policies of the private, nonprofit, and public sectors that affect our society every day. Generally speaking, having a good quality of life distinguishes between merely living and living well (or well-being). It implies having the opportunity to live life to its fullest potential; having access to a healthy, clean, and pleasurable environment; and enjoying social, environmental, and economic justice.

Efforts to improve the quality of life have been a reaction, at least in part, to sprawling growth patterns. As people living in suburbs spend increasing amounts of time in their cars fighting traffic and less time interacting with their families and communities, they may feel a growing sense of frustration and isolation.

At the same time, sprawl may affect the quality of life of the people left behind in the cities. People living in decaying cities may suffer from high air pollution, fewer job opportunities, poor water quality, crime, insufficient schools, or crumbling infrastructure.

Wildland—Urban Interface

Increasing numbers of Americans are choosing to live in the small towns and open spaces (known as gateway communities) that surround our magnificent national and state parks, wildlife refuges, forests, wilderness areas, and other public lands.[37] As more people have built houses in the forest, we have expanded an area known as the wildland–urban interface. New developments in and around forest areas and grasslands have increased the risk of wildfires near human habitation. Once largely considered California's problem, residential fire losses associated with wildland fires gained national attention in 1985 when 1,400 homes were destroyed nationwide.[38]

Wildland–urban interface fires are a significant concern for residents, as well as for federal, state, and local land management and fire agencies. Research is under way to better understand the causes of the fires, methods to prevent damage, and residents' perceptions of fire management policies. In the meantime, those who choose to build in those areas accept a certain risk. Our current understanding of fire ecology tells us that fire prevention is neither possible nor desirable; therefore, homeowners who live in and near wildlands should take on the responsibility of ensuring the safety of their property.[39] Increased fire risk is just one more example of a societal impact as humans spread into new areas.[40]

Other problems occurring along the wildland–urban interface include the spread of invasive species into forest ecosystems, alteration of natural waterways caused by development and by increases in impervious surfaces, and forest fragmentation. Furthermore, competing interests meet along the interface because some people want development to continue while others want to protect forestland. For more information about issues in the wildland–urban interface, see www.nifc.gov and www.interfacesouth.org.

Gentrification and Affordability

Expanding the housing choices for residents is a growing priority for many communities. Strong neighborhoods are typically diverse neighborhoods that provide housing for different ages, family sizes, and income levels. In many cases, however, increased demand for housing has resulted in an increase in housing prices and, subsequently, a reduction in diversity. Existing residents may no longer be able to afford to live in the city neighborhoods where they grew up as those neighborhoods experience *gentrification*. Gentrification can be described as the displacement of lower-income city dwellers by higher-income professionals. In many cities, this ongoing change, coupled with condo conversion, has driven up urban real estate prices and reduced the number of rental units available, thereby causing concern over the availability of affordable housing.[41] Today, some communities are striving to increase housing choices for all income levels by ensuring construction of housing units of different sizes and types and by implementing affordable housing policies and incentives for developers.

Sense of Community

Some people believe that a sense of place has been lost in the transition from "neighborhoods" to what we now call "subdivisions" or "developments."[42] In the modern suburb, people are less likely to interact with their neighbors. They are less likely to walk anywhere, and they tend to spend less time socializing in public spaces, therefore minimizing casual contact with others. People today also tend to have less leisure time because they spend more time in the car or at work.[43] Increasingly, we are on the move and are losing some of the connections that may have helped bond communities in past decades. Those factors, together with the overall homogenization of the places we live in, can effectively reduce our overall sense of community. Yet, efforts are under way to help foster a sense of community. For example, some new developments have reoriented homes toward the street, encouraged front porches, reduced setbacks from the curb, and promoted communities that are friendly toward pedestrians, bicycles, and other means of transit.

Health

Community design, transportation plans, and land use decisions can also affect public health. According to the Centers for Disease Control and Prevention (CDC), one-third of adults get little or no exercise. The lack of exercise is one factor that has led to a rise in adult and child obesity.[44] (More than 3 in 10 adults are overweight, as are one-fourth of youths aged 6 to 17 years.) Certain community design principles increase opportunities for walking and bicycling, which can lead to improved health.

Building schools, shopping centers, and other places of interest that are accessible only by car can prevent people from safely walking, riding bicycles, or playing outdoors. Today, youths between the ages of 5 and 15 do not walk or ride their bicycles as much as they once did. (Thirty years ago, 60 percent of children walked or rode bikes to get to school; today the national average is 13 percent.) The CDC and other organizations are advocating "active community environments" that promote physical activity and have sidewalks; on-street bicycle facilities, parks, paths and trails; and recreational facilities.[45]

Searching for Solutions

We need to rethink our planning ideas so that neighborhood stores, neighborhood institutions, neighborhood gathering places will have a better chance of coming into being and giving heart to the community.

—Philip Langdon (A)

Land in the United States seemed almost limitless in frontier days. Today, however, we are increasingly confronted with our finite supply of land resources. More and more, we must choose between using land for one purpose or another. How we will design our future communities remains to be seen, but that concept will likely depend—at least in part—on the outcome of the debate over land use.

As individuals and as a society, we are constantly changing the world around us and making decisions about our future. Concerns about sprawling development have given rise to alternative ideas on how to respond to the challenges of growth as we design our future communities. The smart growth movement has emerged to encourage citizens and planners to slow urban sprawl into the countryside and thus to preserve natural places and build a sense of community among urban dwellers.

The Future

We all have the potential to influence policy makers, corporations, developers, our communities, and our environment. The decisions we make will have local and far-reaching implications. If we study the positions of candidates and vote for those whose views benefit our neighborhoods, we play a role in the democratic process. If we become informed citizens and join a committee to protect a park or if we join a local planning commission, we become a positive force in our communities. To find out about land ballot measures, please visit www.tpl.org.

Perhaps our most powerful tools for influencing the future are our individual choices and voices. We all face the demands of change. Change and development are inevitable. But, the way we respond to the challenge is up to us. We can choose to either make our voices heard in our communities and thus shape the future, or sit by and watch change happen—for better or for worse. A first step is education.

Endnotes

1 Stegner 1992 (A).
2 U.S. Census Bureau, 2004 (E).
3 Mumford 1961 (A).
4 Vallianatos 1994 (A).
5 U.S. Census Bureau 2004 (E).
6 Gillham 2002 (A).
7 U.S. Department of Agriculture 2001 (E).
8 Ibid.
9 Ibid.
10 Ibid.
11 Fulton et al. 2001 (E).
12 Friedman 2002 (A).
13 Gillham 2002 (A).
14 Benfield, Raimi, and Chen 1999 (A).
15 Gillham 2002 (A).
16 Benfield, Terris, and Vorsanger 2001 (A).
17 Gillham 2002 (A).
18 Beach 2002 (E).
19 Ibid.
20 U.S. Census Bureau 2001 (E).
21 EPA 2001 (C).
22 O'Meara 1999 (C).
23 Gillham 2002 (A).
24 Benfield et al. 1999 (A).
25 Ibid.
26 Gillham 2002 (A).
27 Ibid.
28 Columbia University's CIESIN 2003 (E).
29 Caballero 2003 (B).
30 Gillham 2002 (A).
31 Benfield et al. 1999 (A).
32 Ibid.
33 Gillham 2002 (A).
34 The Road Information Program (TRIP) 2000 (E).
35 Duany et al. 2000 (A).
36 Library of Congress 2002 (E).
37 Howe et al. 1997 (A).
38 Cohen 2000 (B).
39 Ibid.
40 See Project Learning Tree's secondary module Exploring Environmental Issues:Focus on Forests for more information and activities on the wildland–urban interface.
41 Gillham 2002 (A).
42 State of Maryland 2001 (C).
43 Langdon 1994 (A).
44 Centers for Disease Control and Prevention 2003 (E).
45 Centers for Disease Control and Prevention 2000 (C).

Letters following author and date citations refer to sections in the bibliography (Appendix B) where the reader can find full data about the sources cited.

Personal Places

Students investigate and report on their connection with a special place and with their greater community.

1

Subjects
Earth Studies, Geography, History, Social Studies

Concepts
1.10 Natural beauty, as experienced in forests and other habitats, enhances the quality of human life by providing artistic and spiritual inspiration, as well as recreational and intellectual opportunities.

2.4 Resource management technologies interact and influence environmental quality; the acquisition, extraction, and transportation of natural resources; all life forms; and each other.

2.10 Cultural and societal perspectives influence the attitudes, beliefs, and biases of people toward the use of resources and environmental protection.

3.8 Most cultures have beliefs, values, and traditions that shape human interactions with the environment and its resources.

Skills
Analyzing, Identifying Attributes and Components, Identifying Main Ideas, Observing, Reasoning

Materials
Large paper, crayons, map of your community, copies of student pages, thumbtacks or dot stickers, sheet or tarp (optional)

Time Considerations
Three 50-minute periods

Objectives
▶ Students will convey their connection to the place in which they live through visual, oral, and written means.

▶ Students will identify the positive and negative attributes of their community.

▶ Students will create a map of special places in their community.

▶ Students will analyze what makes their community unique.

Assessments
▶ Ask students to interview a parent or guardian about a special place from his or her childhood, and find out why it was important. Does it still exist? Has it changed? Have students report back to the class and provide a written summary of why the place is or was special.

▶ Revisit the question "What makes your community special?" and have students write an essay response.

▶ Following the model of the Pine Barrens or another selected case study, encourage students to write a similar case study based on what they have learned about their own community.

Background

We all react, consciously and unconsciously, to the places where we live and work, in ways we scarcely notice or that are only now becoming known to us.... Our ordinary surroundings, built and natural alike, have an immediate and a continuing effect on the way we feel and act, and on our health and intelligence.

—Tony Hiss (A)

What Is Sense of Place?

Place is more than just a location or a spot on a map. Place is inextricably linked with people: people create places when they endow locations with cultural and natural values. People share experiences; invent and celebrate rituals and traditions; and visually and physically change the landscape by creating farmland, building dams, digging tunnels, and erecting buildings. In the process, they build and occupy places. By altering an area or intentionally leaving it "as is," people put their stamp on a place.

A **sense of place** is a special collection of qualities and characteristics, visual, cultural, social, and environmental that provides meaning to location. A sense of place is one of many connections that individuals can develop with their local environment, whether the environment is urban, suburban, or rural, built or natural. A sense of place is what makes an environment psychologically comfortable.[1]

When speaking of a sense of place, people might refer to architectural beauty, natural beauty, spirit, quality of life offered, or livability. Others might mention the flavor, climate, feeling, ambience, essence, presence, harmony, grace, charm, or seemliness.[2]

Why Is Sense of Place Important?

Sense of place makes your hometown different from my hometown and that which makes your physical place worth caring about.

—Ed McMahon (B)

A sense of place provides a sense of belonging, of commitment. It is a place of family and community ties, or roots, that stem from our connection to a particular location and its people. Feeling connected fosters a sense of caring for place, which promotes stewardship. In short, the stronger our sense of place, the more we care about and for our surroundings and our communities.[3]

Thus, a sense of place may spur greater concern for farmland, parks, cities, neighborhoods, and the environment in general. Much of the interest in environmental conservation, farmland preservation, historic preservation, **scenic** conservation, and neighborhood protection derives from people's strong connection to place and their reaction to threats against it. For example, the **smart growth** movement is a reaction to the loss of community character as a result of rapid, low-density growth and the influx of franchise development—otherwise known as **sprawl**.

Understanding place is the cornerstone for effecting community change. Improving the quality of life, engaging in environmental stewardship, creating more sustainable cultures and communities, transforming neighborhoods, and building community can occur when people are invested in their community and their roots.[4]

A Sense of Connection

If you don't know where you are, you don't know who you are.

—Wendell Berry in *The Sense of Place* by Wallace Stegner (A)

There are many ways in which "connectedness" to and within a place can manifest itself. One can be connected to the natural aspects of the landscape that one inhabits such as rolling farmland. Other people may feel a connection to the human and human-made elements of a place, including a place's history or built features like the Manhattan skyline.[5] Many of us have special connections with specific places in our communities that offer a sense of belonging, deep contentment, or attachment. We may be connected to where we were born, the house we grew up in, or where we spent time with friends and family, for example.

Nature and Sense of Place

I do not know whether it is possible to love the planet or not, but I do know that it is possible to love the places we can see, touch, smell, and experience.

—David Orr, Earth in Mind (A)

Sense of place is intimately linked to our natural surroundings. An expanding body of research shows that almost all of us rely on nature—whether it is sprouting from a flowerpot or stretching as far as the eye can see—to excite our senses, restore our nerves, invite us to play, enhance our social bonds, and supply meaning and metaphor to our lives.[6]

Childhood exploration in the natural world can be a key ingredient in developing a sense of place. Robert Michael Pyle wrote about his childhood adventures of exploring a weedy ditch "on the wrong side of Denver." Pyle believes that "most people have a ditch somewhere—or a creek, meadow, woodlot, or marsh.... These are places of initiation, where the borders between ourselves and other creatures break down, where the earth gets under our nails and a sense of place gets under our skin."[7]

Yet there is concern that many youths today are growing up with fewer connections to the natural world and are typically spending more and more time inside. Until recently, a large majority of the world's population lived in

Copyright Project for Public Spaces, Inc. www.pps.org

villages, but in 2000, approximately half of the world's population lived in cities.[8] (See Figure 1.1.)

The percentage of children who have frequent exposure to wildlands and to undomesticated species is smaller than ever before in human history.[9] As more people move to cities, one challenge will be strengthening communities and helping urban children connect with their places through the creation of safe passages, preservation of open spaces, and reductions in crime.

Nurturing a Sense of Place

Of all the memberships we identify ourselves by (racial, ethnic, sexual, national, age, religious, occupational), the one that is most forgotten and that has the greatest potential for healing is place.... Community values come from deliberately, knowledgeably, and affectionately "living in place."

—Gary Snyder

To foster a sense of place, communities must support **built environments** and settlement patterns that are uplifting and memorable and that create a special feeling of belonging. A community also nurtures a sense of place by understanding and respecting its natural context—unique elements such as its rivers, hilltops, open lands, and native plants and wildlife. Another important step is respecting and preserving community landmarks

Figure 1.1 Population living in suburban areas

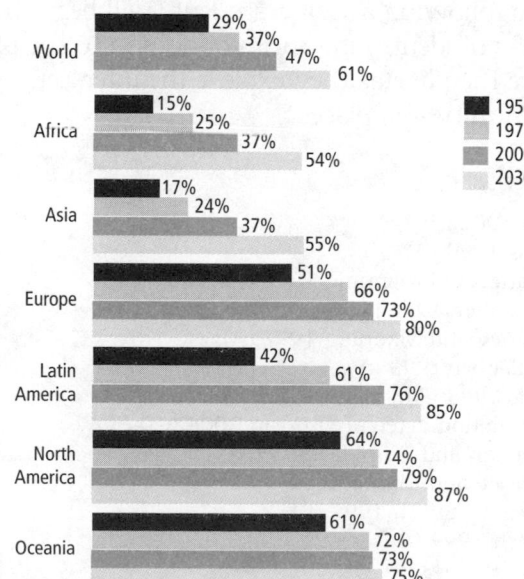

Note: The United Nations cautions users that the definition of "urban" varies by country.
Source: United Nations, World Urbanization Prospects: The 2003 Revision, 2004 (C).

such as a civic monument, local diner, historic courthouse, scenic vista, or clock tower.[10] Our increasing mobility as a society may challenge our ability to develop a sense of place in our communities. "In the United States we are a people on the move. Forced by necessity or drawn by desire, we pack up and leave one place and community for another seeking new opportunities or wealth at a rate unheard of in earlier societies."[11] To develop a sense of place, people need to feel invested in their communities and need not see them simply as interim stopping points on the way to somewhere else.

Technology also raises interesting questions about fostering a sense of place. Cellular phones, the Internet, fax machines, and overnight couriers have made it possible for more people to live and work wherever they choose, with or without attachment to place. Even industries themselves have become increasingly "footloose," as many are no longer constrained by traditional needs such as access to rivers or railroads. This new freedom of choice among workers and industries is reshaping the geography of America. Some people see the digital economy fracturing the metropolis as people become increasingly removed, physically and socially, from their communities. As people spend less time interacting with the natural and built environment, communities might suffer from lack of attention and reduced personal and financial investment.

However, it is also possible that technologies such as the Internet and cellular phones will bring people closer together. The Internet connects millions of previously isolated people by providing a means to exchange new ideas. In addition, certain places that offer a unique environment, such as downtowns, could

have a competitive advantage over those that don't. If people have greater choices in where to live and work, they may select places that offer special recreational and cultural amenities such as restaurants, theaters, museums, professional sports arenas, and access to the outdoors.

Place and Community

Place and community are often intertwined, but they are not always the same. Generally speaking, we often refer to communities as the places we live. Yet a community has come to mean practically any group of people joined together by almost any shared characteristic (e.g., academic, racial, corporate, ethnic, or sexual). It does not necessarily relate to a concrete geographic location. In fact, a community does not even need to be tied to a fixed location, although it often is. For example, nomads, gypsies, or even members of a traveling circus may form a community, but they do not necessarily occupy a particular place, at least not for long. Place, however, may signify community, but its meaning is bound to some geographical location.[12] Sense of place can be described as defining oneself in terms of a given piece of land.[13] In essence, sense of place is inseparably linked with a physical landscape—the communities where we all live and work.

In the following activity, students will begin the process of identifying their connection to the place where they live as they explore the intersection of community and place.

Endnotes

1   Xu 2002 (E).
2   Hiss 1990 (A).
3   Beatley and Manning 1997 (A).
4   Mullahey 1998 (C).
5   Beatley and Manning 1997 (A).
6   Gallagher 1993 (A).
7   Pyle 1993 (A).
8   Population Reference Bureau 2004 (C).
9   Nabhan and Trimble 1995 (A).
10 Beatley and Manning 1997 (A).
11 Gregory Smith 1997 (B).
12 Leach 1999 (A).
13 Xu 1995 (E).

Letters following author and date citations refer to sections in the bibliography (Appendix B) where the reader can find full data about the sources cited.

- Enlarge a map of your neighborhood or town. (If you do not have a local map, maps.yahoo.com or www.mapquest.com to generate one, or visit the nearest office of the American Automobile Association, your town hall, or a local visitors' center to obtain a free map.)
- Make copies of student page "My Place." *Optional*: Make copies of the student pages "Case Study: New Jersey Pine Barrens."
- *Optional*: Find a large sheet or tarp to conceal your students' pictures or models of their favorite places before displaying them.

Doing the Activity

1. Ask the students to think back in time to when they were about 10 years old. Where did they live? What was their neighborhood like? Where did they play? Where did their friends live? Hand out a large sheet of paper and crayons, and have the students draw a map from memory showing the location of their house and the features of their neighborhood. Have them include all the features that they can remember, such as buildings, roads, parks, fields, streams, and their friends' residences. Let each student share his or her drawing with another student or with the class. What were some common features that they remembered? Have things changed in their neighborhood? What has caused the change? Have the changes been improvements, or have they had a negative impact?

2. Ask students to think about the community where they live today, in terms of its physical location, its visual character, and its place in modern society and culture. Then ask students to write their answers to the following questions:
- Is your community special to you? Why or why not?
- Can you identify special qualities of your community? Are they visual, physical, cultural, natural, or built qualities? Are they positive or negative?
- Do you think other people would see those features of your community as special? Why or why not?

3. Invite several students to share their answers. If students do not consider their community special, challenge them to think of what they would change to make it a special place.

4. Ask students to think of a physical place within the community that *is* special to them. There are no right or wrong answers; students might pick their home, park, street, restaurant, store, tree, or stream.

5. Hand out copies of "Student Page: My Place" for students to complete.

6. For homework, assign students the task of visiting their place and creating a visual representation of it to bring to class. They can take a photograph, draw a picture, or create a model. In addition, you might have students write a poem, short story, or journal entry about their place. Notify students that they will be asked to share their place with the rest of the class.

7. Back in class, collect all the pictures, models, and other representations, and display them in your classroom (but keep the display covered until step 9).

8. Divide the class into groups of three or four students. In their groups, have students share their answers to "My Place." Then encourage the groups to explore the following questions:
- Were places selected because they were visually pleasing? Comfortable?
- Do you go to this place to be alone or to socialize?
- What senses do you use in your place?
- How are the places similar? Different?
- How many of the places are natural? Built? Both?
- What types of places were not chosen? Why?

9. Unveil the display of all the places, and give students time to observe. What kinds of places have they selected? Ask a few students to share their place with the whole class and to explain some of the points they mentioned in their small groups. Or have several students read what they wrote about their place, and ask the rest of the class to identify which visual goes with it.

10. Introduce the sense of place concept by asking students to come up with a definition. As they discuss their ideas, refer to the "Background" information found in this section. *Note*: There is no one definition for sense of place; however, students should identify that having a sense of place is part of what makes a place worth caring about or exhibiting environmental stewardship for.

11. Using the enlarged map of your community, ask students to locate and mark their special places (try using thumbtacks or dot stickers).

12. Display the marked map, and discuss how the students' special places fit into the larger community and how those places may give the students a sense of place with respect to where they live.

- Let students create a visitor's guide for their community that highlights all their special places.

- Invite students to read or listen to a description of Walden Pond. Discuss the attributes that Henry David Thoreau (A) found so stimulating and rewarding. Or have students read Aldo Leopold's *A Sand County Almanac* (A) or *A Tree Grows in Brooklyn* by Betty Smith (A). Then have students think and write about a natural area in poetry or prose, or have them compare and contrast their local natural area to those in the books they read.

- Ask students to write a short piece describing how technology might affect sense of place. For example, does technology influence whether children, adults, or both are spending more or less time outside or are socializing in public spaces? Do technologies such as the Internet, video games, television, and cell phones threaten or enhance our sense of place?

- Plan a field trip to explore one or more of the students' special places.

Enrichment

- Share with your students a case study about sense of place, such as the example of "New Jersey Pine Barrens." As a class, discuss how your community compares to the Pine Barrens. Links to additional case studies are available on PLT's website at www.plt.org. Discuss which elements connote a sense of place.

- Interview three different people from your community who represent different generations. Possible age groupings could be 0–15 years, 25–50 years, and 51–80 years. Ask those individuals what is special about the community? What makes the community unique? Have students compare their findings.

My Place

1. Name a place in your community that is special to you.

2. What makes this place unique or special to you?

3. When and how did you discover your place?

4. What are the natural and built components of your place?

5. What do you do at this place? Or what have you done there?

6. Do you think your place will change in the future? Why? How?

7. Do you want it to change? Why or why not?

8. How would you feel if your place disappeared?

9. How does your place fit into the rest of your community?

Case Study: New Jersey Pine Barrens

With more than one million acres, the New Jersey Pine Barrens provides many unique places for residents and visitors alike to explore and enjoy. Located in the Atlantic Coastal Plain within the southeastern portion of the state, the New Jersey Pine Barrens is the largest open space on the eastern seaboard between Boston, Massachusetts, and Richmond, Virginia. As early as 1895, people were recommending that this unique area be protected for its water resources, recreational opportunities, natural beauty, forestry, and scientific importance.

The human history of the New Jersey Pine Barrens is tied to use of the region's abundant natural resources. It is believed that the earliest residents of the Pine Barrens, the Lenape Indians, arrived after the last glacier left New Jersey—about 12,000 years ago. The glaciers reached just north of the Pine Barrens, and the melted glaciers covered the sand and gravel of the Coastal Plain. When Europeans arrived in the mid-17th century, the Native Americans whom they encountered lived a foraging and farming existence. The Lenape used many of the area's resources by hunting, trapping, fishing, and gathering. They also moved seasonally throughout the region to fish shad from rivers in the spring and to tend gardens, and travel to the shore, hunt, dig or rake clams, and gather eggs in the summer.

Lumbering and Farming

The early European settlers were at first intimidated by the unbroken forest. It represented danger – from Native Americans, wild animals, and fires. Eventually, by the early 1700's, they established a forest industry in the Pine Barrens. They cut trees for cordwood, lumber, charcoal, paper, tar, and turpentine. Atlantic white cedar was the highly prized species for lumbering in the Pine Barrens, because the trees produce very lightweight, straight-grained wood that is rot, weather, and disease resistant. The wood was valuable throughout the region for framing and

siding homes, fence posts, roofs, crates, furniture, boats, and even locally produced decoys—a traditional craft still carried on in the region today.

Farming for food and income is another traditional activity in the Pine Barrens that continues today. The different regions of the Pine Barrens have lent themselves to different types of farming, such as cranberry growing in wet, boggy areas and blueberry cultivation in damp, sandy areas. On the edge of the Pine Barrens on soils that could support fruit and vegetable crops, truck and row-crop farming were possible. Cranberries were first cultivated in logged over cedar swamps where bog iron had been mined out. The wild cranberry, *Vaccinium macrocarpon*, is a trailing evergreen vine that is native to sandy, peat bogs of North America. Cranberries grow naturally in open wetlands and along the rivers and streams in the Pine Barrens. Early agriculturists gathered the berries for domestic consumption and commercial use. The success of cranberry cultivation has turned the village of Chatsworth in the Pine Barrens into the cranberry capital of New Jersey. The cultivation of the blueberry also came from a small Pine Barrens village, Whitesbog. Elizabeth White, daughter of Whitesbog cranberry grower J. J. White, wanted to cultivate the wild blueberries that grew in the nearby swamps and bogs. Many other farmers

Case Study: New Jersey Pine Barrens (cont.)

had tried without success, adhering to the generally accepted belief that blueberries could not be cultivated from the forests. Still, Elizabeth White was interested, and she asked local woodsmen to collect blueberry plants from the swamps around the state. Her partnership with U.S. Department of Agriculture official, Dr. Frederick Coville, and several years of research at Whitesbog resulted in the first successof blueberries in 1916.

The history of lumbering and agriculture is vital to understanding the Pine Barrens, its ecology, the residents of the area, and the unique connection between the people and the land that leads to a sense of place. Resource-based communities in the Pine Barrens developed with the wood products industry and were sustained by regional advances in agriculture—especially advances related to cranberries and blueberries.

Iron

Other industries had a widespread effect on the region. Iron furnaces and glassmaking supported large populations in the Pine Barrens from the mid-1700s to nearly the end of the 1800s, with an economic peak in the 1840s. Iron forges and furnaces dotted the riverside from north to south in the Pine Barrens. The locations of almost all the furnaces are now known, although not much remains of them. Iron production required a tremendous amount of wood fuel, chiefly pitch pine, which was harvested from nearby stands and burned into charcoal. To make 12,000 bushels of charcoal, 6,000 cords of wood were needed. The charcoal was used to fire furnaces that produced from 700 to 900 tons of iron per year. The raw material was bog iron, or limonite, which was found in the swamps along the streams of the Pine Barrens. Once the ore was dug and transported to the furnace, it was crushed into small pieces and smelted over a hot fire. Some products of the iron furnaces in the Pine Barrens were cannon balls, cast-iron stoves, pots, pans,

ax heads, shovels, and water pipes. Forges located near the furnaces smelted the iron from the furnaces into brittle pig iron (crude iron tapped from a blast furnace), which could be used to make stoves, kettles, sash weights, and fire backs. After repeated hammering and reheating, some of the pig iron was turned into more supple wrought iron, which could be used to fashion tools, horseshoes, and wagon tires.

Moving On

Natural resources in the Pine Barrens served a thriving economy, and industries prospered throughout the area. A decrease in the availability of raw materials contributed to the initial decline of Pine Barrens society. Communities moved from one area to another as the tree resource was depleted. At first, many people moved westward in search of success and wealth, leaving deserted stagecoach towns and once-booming industries to literally crumble or become susceptible to forest fires. Later, when the iron industry collapsed as a result of the over harvesting of the forest and the discovery of coal in western Pennsylvania, many more residents departed. Left behind were the deteriorating foundations of factories, forges, and villages that became known as the forgotten or lost towns of the Pine Barrens.

Pineys

Still, some people remained in the area, adapted to the change in lifestyle and pace of life, and found a source of income and economic survival elsewhere. Some of those people refer to themselves as "Natives", "Locals", or "Pineys." Typically, Pineys have lived in the region for their entire lives. Many Pineys are from multi-generational local families and are living resource-based lives to some extent. Some can find their way from the northern end to the southern end of the pines by using only sand roads. And some observe the seasonality of life in the pines, picking blueberries in the spring, fishing and clamming in the summer, picking cranberries in the fall, and

Case Study: New Jersey Pine Barrens (cont.)

harvesting pinecones and laurels in the winter. In the Pine Barrens, nearly all sand roads, streams, hills, and ponds have place names.

Protection of the Pine Barrens

Development pressure on the Pine Barrens increased as the population of New Jersey soared in the 1950s and 1960s; people fled from urban areas to the expanding suburbs and diminishing rural parts of the state. In 1978, after much debate and many local public hearings about proposals, President Jimmy Carter signed the National Parks and Recreation Act, whose reach extended to the Pine Barrens. This act designated approximately one million acres of the Pine Barrens area as the Pinelands National Reserve. A year later, the New Jersey Pinelands Protection Act took effect to implement the federal act and to ensure the protection of the Pinelands by establishing a regional planning and management commission. Then in 1983, the United Nations Educational, Scientific and Cultural Organization (UNESCO) designated the Pine Barrens as a Biosphere Reserve by the U.S. Man and the Biosphere Program.

Protection of Natural Resources

The Pine Barrens contains a rich variety of natural resources that have been used and appreciated for centuries by people living in the area. For example, water is a vital resource in the Pine Barrens—so vital that it prompted, in part, the original legislation to protect the area. The Pine Barrens is the site of the Kirkwood-Cohansey aquifer, an underground reservoir that contains 17 trillion gallons of fresh water. Bogs and streams form where the aquifer approaches the surface. The sandy, acidic soil contains iron, which combined with tannic acid from leaves, gives the water a rusty, tea-like color. The bogs and swamps of the Pine Barrens, provide suitable habitat for 21 northern plant species, including turkey beard (*Xerophyllum asphodeloides*), to reach their southernmost limits in the Pine Barrens. At the same time, 110 plant species

that are typically found in the south, such as sand myrtle (*Leiophyllum buxifolium*), reach their northernmost limits in the Pine Barrens. Broom crowberry (*Corema conradii*) is an example of an endangered plant species that is limited to the upland Pine Plains because of frequent fires.

Many animals, including several protected and rare species, can be found in the area. Perhaps the most well known but seldom seen animal associated with the area is the elusive Pine Barrens tree frog, *Hyla andersonii*. This amphibian lives in seasonally wet areas of the Pine Barrens, and you can hear its call on warm humid spring and summer nights throughout the pines. White-tailed deer, red and gray foxes, rabbits, squirrels, and pine snakes also make their home in the Pine Barrens.

Fire plays a major role in the ecology of the Pine Barrens, creating periodic disturbances in the plant succession. Forest fires were once used as a tool by the Native Americans. The New Jersey Forest Fire Service now uses prescribed burns to control the threat of wildfires and to improve forest health.

Natural and cultural resources combine to create a unique sense of place in the New Jersey Pine Barrens. People from around the world have traveled to explore this special ecosystem that is found in the most densely populated state in the country. Generations of families still own and operate farms, while others hunt, fish, kayak, and lead tours of forgotten towns within the Pine Barrens. With greater understanding of its ecology and culture, more residents and visitors alike will be able to experience a sense of place in the New Jersey Pine Barrens.

For more information, please visit www.state.nj.us/pinelands, www.whitesbog.org, www.unesco.org/mab, and www.nj.gov/dep/parksandforests/forest/.

Community Character

Students explore community character and investigate the ways that communities, including their own, are responding to growth and development pressures.

2

Subjects
Ecology, Environmental Science, Photography, and Social Studies

Concepts
2.10 Cultural and societal perspectives influence the attitudes, beliefs, and biases of people toward the use of resources and environmental protection.

3.4 Ecosystems possess measurable indicators of environmental health.

5.4 Ecosystems change over time through patterns of growth and succession. They are also affected by other phenomena such as disease, insects, fire, weather, climate, and human intervention.

Skills
Analyzing, Defining Problems, Identifying Attributes and Components, Observing, Problem Solving, Researching, Summarizing

Materials
Copies of student pages.
Optional: cameras

Time Considerations
Part A: Two 50-minute periods

Part B: One or two 50-minute periods

Part C: Three or four 50-minute periods

Objectives
▶ Students will conduct a field survey and will determine what adds to—and detracts from—their community's character.

▶ Students will examine the ways that change affects their community's character.

▶ Students will research a local land use issue and will analyze its effect on their community's character.

▶ Students will relate the idea of community character to their sense of place.

Assessments
▶ Ask students to read the student page case study "Dudley Street Neighborhood Initiative" and answer the following questions:

▶ What threatened the Dudley Street neighborhood's character?

▶ How did the residents implement change?

▶ How did the changes affect community character?

▶ How is the Dudley Street case study similar to or different from the Smoky Mountains case study?

▶ How are issues in the Dudley Street case study similar to or different from issues in your community?

▶ Have students design individual collages or multimedia presentations highlighting the visual aspects that they value in their community. Some students might develop a presentation highlighting visual characteristics that both add to and detract from their community's character. The final products might be displayed at school, the town library, or the chamber of commerce.

▶ Invite students to write a letter to the editor of a local paper to suggest ideas for enhancing the sense of place or sense of community for local residents.

Background

Change is inevitable, but it does not have to come at the expense of what citizens and communities value. We can either be victims of change or we can plan for it, shape it, and emerge stronger from it. The choice is ours.

—Jim Howe, Ed McMahon, and Luther Propst (A)

Has your neighborhood changed significantly over the past few years? Are the cultural character and the **visual character** of your community changing? More likely than not, the answer to those questions is "yes," because many communities around the country are experiencing the effects of rapid growth and development. In some areas, agricultural fields and forests are being paved to accommodate new housing subdivisions, shopping centers, roads, and parking lots. In some urban neighborhoods, luxury buildings are replacing older, historical housing units and shops. Those new buildings can be unaffordable to many residents but can also provide more income for the city. Communities all over the country are facing the loss of **green space**, **scenic viewsheds**, trees, recreation areas, and **visual integrity**. What can we do to help communities integrate change and retain their character?

What Is Community Character?

Community character defies any singular definition. Each community must decide for itself what defines its character. A rural community might take pride in its intimate main street, healthy forests, agricultural products, historic battlefields or its viewshed of unique natural features such as expansive farmlands, deserts, rivers, mountain ranges, or oceans. City residents might note world-renowned skyscrapers, vibrant commercial districts, or city parks as some of the distinguishing features of their community. Suburban residents might take comfort in green lawns, children playing in the street, people walking dogs, and front porches. Asking residents key questions can help them define the essence of community character. You might ask these: What distinguishes your town from others? What are your favorite aspects of your town? Where do you take out-of-town visitors? What are your town's natural assets? What are its environmental, social, cultural, economic, educational, and historic strengths and weaknesses? What organizations or groups are effective at bringing residents together?

Certain elements contribute to a strong sense of community character. A community must have strong connections between individuals—otherwise known as social capital. The interactions between residents are necessary to build a community. Strong bonds are created through trust, reciprocity, and shared values and behaviors; they foster commitment between

residents and a sense of belonging. Social capital allows citizens to voice and resolve problems—resulting in smooth advancement for the community. Furthermore, communities with strong social capital experience less crime, better health, higher educational achievement, and better economic growth. Social capital is the glue that holds a community together.[1]

A community also needs a solid **social infrastructure** provided by social institutions such as places of worship, political associations, and recreational groups, which provide social cohesion. Those institutions allow individuals to spend time and develop bonds with other residents who share similar interests. Within those groups, there need to be strong human resources; people with organizational skills, varied educational credentials, and similar social, ethnic, racial, and cultural backgrounds bring residents together and establish effective associations. However, social infrastructure is ineffective without social capital, and vice versa.[2]

Change and Character

Communities have always evolved and changed; however, change is occurring faster today than ever before. For example, over the past 25 years, we have created—virtually from scratch—new, decentralized cities at the urban fringe. Those suburban cities (also called "edge cities") surround all our major metropolitan areas, usually in the form of high-rise office buildings, stand-alone hotels and condominiums, housing complexes, and sprawling regional malls. The new growth is often clustered around highway interchanges, which have overtaken waterways and railroad junctions as the preferred locations for business and industry.

Current growth trends are leading us toward a more homogenized country, thereby threatening our **sense of place** and community. Distinguishing one town, suburb, or city from another becomes increasingly difficult as chain restaurants and stores spread across the United States. The idea that "every place looks like every other place" is increasingly a local and national concern. What traditionally distinguished one community from another was its unique history, visual character, and cultural and natural resources—its neighborhoods and skyline, social and economic values, parks, and people. According to the National Park Service, preserving the historic character of our neighborhoods may become the most fundamental act of conservation and preservation.[3]

Whether change results from population shifts, industrial or commercial expansion, urban flight, or **gentrification**, many communities are experiencing character change. Yet such change need not be negative or equated with loss of character. Community character is constantly changing because of increasing cultural and economic diversification. The change can enable a new community character to emerge that reflects the needs and wants of current and future citizens. Through active involvement in their communities, individuals can ensure that new development benefits residents and does not remove the desirable characteristics that make their city or town unique. Furthermore, preserving the special qualities of America's communities and landscapes doesn't need to jeopardize economic well-being. Study after study shows that communities that preserve their character and natural values consistently outperform the economies of those that do not.[4]

Community character and quality of life are leading factors in attracting businesses to a new location. Once, it was common for people to move to a new area because of better job prospects. Today, however, studies report that people will move to a new area with a desirable quality of life even if it means taking a job that pays less. Accordingly, businesses relocate to areas that are attracting people. For instance, business owners in the Yellowstone region indicated that they either moved to or remained in that area because of the quality of the environment. They were also influenced by its ideal location to raise a family and its **scenic** beauty. The study reported that "Firms locate in Greater Yellowstone Ecosystem because of environmental, recreational, and community amenities, not for primary business considerations."[5]

Copyright Project for Public Spaces, Inc. www.pps.org

Visual Pollution

The visual character of a community—that is, the appearance of its streets, neighborhoods, open space, and business areas—is essential to its long-term economic viability and helps determine how residents and visitors alike perceive it.[6] Yet for many American communities, change may also bring visual pollution, which changes the community's visual character. Visual pollution generally refers to what the community defines as unattractive elements of its landscape, such as billboards, inappropriate or large signs, incongruous architecture, strip malls, utility poles, wires, graffiti, cell towers, weeds, bright lights, and litter.[7]

Billboards are one of the worst offenders. According to Scenic America, their ill effects include endangering our health and safety, hampering economic growth, degrading the landscape, and weakening our connection to the environment. Many communities, and some entire states, have chosen to prohibit, regulate, or remove billboards to protect and enhance their scenic character.[8] Billboard control improves community character and quality of life, both of which directly impact local economies. In fact, despite billboard industry claims to the contrary, communities and states that enact tough billboard controls enjoy strong economic growth.[9] A lot of billboards can clutter an area, which in turn makes it hard for advertising to be noticed. Therefore, fewer signs are more effective. Furthermore, some areas allow natural beauty to attract tourist revenue. In that case, billboards hinder economic activity.[10]

Increasingly, communities are seeking creative ways to confront visual pollution. For example, in Jacksonville, Florida, a nonprofit citizens' coalition called JaxPride helps neighborhoods identify and combat visual pollution in their communities.[11] Community volunteers attend an educational seminar and then conduct a neighborhood survey to record elements of visual pollution. JaxPride generates a report based on the volunteers' findings and forwards it to the appropriate agency for action. In other places, some businesses have even made efforts to blend in with the character of the community. For instance, some fastfood franchises have moved into buildings that reflect the characteristic architectural design of the community.

What's in Store for Your Community's Visual, Cultural, and Historic Character?

Are there signs in your neighborhood that changes are occurring or might occur in the near future? What are some of the benefits and costs of community change? How might those changes affect the visual environment? Are there any individuals or groups that would be positively or negatively affected by change? The case studies in this activity follow two communities: one experiencing rapid change and the other working to modify change. Both provide insights into how a community can manage change and how residents can ensure that growth enhances a community's character and its citizens' quality of life.

Source: Scenic America 2000 (E).

Endnotes

1 Mark K. Smith 2002 (E).
2 Besser 1995 (E).
3 National Park Service 2000 (E).
4 Howe, McMahon, and Propst 1997 (A).
5 Ibid.
6 Scenic America 2000 (E).
7 Dunn, Montoya, and White 2000 (E); Scenic America 2000 (E); Dunn Foundation 2002 (E).
8 Scenic America 2000 (E).
9 Ibid.
10 Ibid.
11 JaxPride 2002 (E)

Letters following author and date citations refer to sections in the bibliography (Appendix B) where the reader can find full data about the sources cited.

Getting Ready

• Photocopy the student pages "Character Search" and "Local Land Use Issue."
• Review and copy the case studies "Gateway Communities of the Great Smoky Mountains National Park" and for the assessment, the "Dudley Street Neighborhood Initiative."
• Collect articles dealing with **land use** issues across the country.
• Keep an eye out for local land use issues.
• If possible, obtain cameras for students to use.

Doing the Activity

Part A

1. Divide the class into groups of two or three students, and have group members work together to answer these questions: What does a place you would like to live in look like? What do you not want it to look like? Invite students to use words, drawings, and images to answer the questions.

2. Reconvene for a class discussion and share ideas. Introduce the terms "visual pollution" and "visual character," noting that a community's physical appearance greatly influences its character (or lack thereof). On the board, create a starter list of the elements that help form the visual character of a community. Review it. Have students think of their own community. Which description does it most closely resemble? Is visual pollution an issue in their community?

3. *Optional*: Obtain a copy of the curriculum, *View Finders Too*, to conduct the visual preference survey with your students. (See the "Enrichment" section of this activity for information on how to purchase the curriculum.)

4. Have students work in small groups to explore the visual character of their community. Distribute copies of the student page titled "Character Search," and explain that as part of their investigation, students will conduct a field survey. Depending on your situation and location, the survey might be conducted during class time or assigned for homework. Explain that students don't need to cover their entire community; they should select an area to survey (such as their neighborhood or main street). You might assign students to cover different areas. If cameras are available, encourage students to use them to photograph their findings— both visual pollution and community assets. As another option, have students sketch their findings.

5. Back in class, invite student groups to share their findings. In the follow-up discussion, ask the following questions: How much did individual tastes determine what is visual character and what is pollution? Is the community's character changing? How? Why? What were the visual clues? Were there other clues?

Part B

6. Hand out the case study titled "Great Smoky Mountain Gateway Communities" for students to read.

7. Ask students to discuss the questions at the end of the case study. They may work either as a class or in small groups. As part of the discussion, encourage students to explore the relationship between community character and the community's economy.

Part C

8. Have students list different land use issues that they may be familiar with (e.g., development of open space, construction of new roads, a proposal for a new mall, creation of a mass transit system, habitat protection, rezoning of an area). Share any articles you have collected to explore some current issues about local land use.

9. Have students break into small groups to research a land use issue in their community (from a list generated in step 8) and to write a summary or prepare a presentation of their findings. Distribute copies of the student page "Case Study–Local Land Use Issue" for students to use as a framework. Encourage students to collect articles, take notes from TV or radio broadcasts, visit the library, use the Internet, attend a planning meeting, visit city hall, or review city council minutes. Students might select an issue that threatens their community's character or one that seeks to either preserve or enhance community character. Encourage students to be creative in designing the form of their presentations. For example, groups might stage a mock television or radio interview, write their report in the form of two letters— each representing the views of a different **shareholder**, orchestrate a representative town meeting, or develop a presentation from the perspective of a concerned citizens league.

10. Give students one or two class periods, plus homework time, to complete their analysis and to prepare a presentation.

11. Invite the groups to share their findings with the class. Create a list of the issues on the board. As each group presents, the other students should write down one or two questions for the presenters. After each presentation, allow time for the questions.

12. To conclude, use the questions below to guide a discussion:

- Is a community's visual character important? Why?
- How can land use decisions affect community character?
- Can environmental protection affect community character?
- What do you think brings about community change?
- Who is responsible for decisions about community character?
- Is there a connection between land use, visual pollution, and community character?
- What are some laws and policies that can control visual pollution?
- What steps can help improve community character?
- Is your community's character threatened? What can you do?
- Is there a connection between community character and sense of place?

Enrichment

- Do a GreenWorks! action project designed to help preserve or enhance community character. For more information about GreenWorks! grants for service-learning projects, see PLT's website at www.plt.org.

- Encourage students to develop journals or posters using photos to document their findings from the community survey. If students have access to digital cameras, they might develop a multimedia presentation. The final products can be shared with other classes or community groups and officials and could lead to a discussion of a vision for the future.

- As a research extension, have students find out if your community has a sign **ordinance**, architectural guidelines, or other regulations designed to influence the community's visual character.

- Have students attend a planning and zoning or a city council meeting.

- Expand this activity by using the *ViewFinders Too* materials developed by The Dunn Foundation. *ViewFinders Too* is a middle school program that provides students with the skills and tools to:

  - explore and analyze the visual enviroment within their own community;
  - provide them with the resources and opportunity to compare and contrast their communities visual environment with the visual environments found in communities in other locations;
  - introduce and teach how to use tools available to bring about change or sustain the visual environment and community character;
  - students are challenged to look at their communities critically and creatively develop their vision of the future.

For further information and to order the materials visit www.dunnfoundation.org

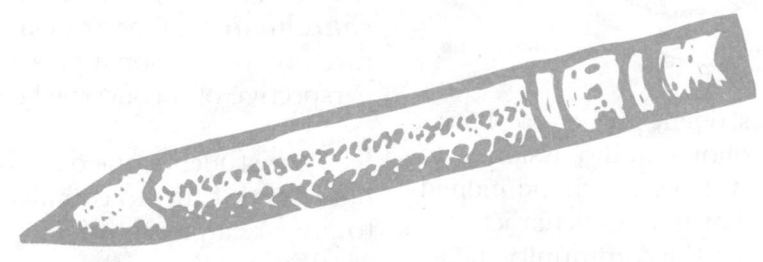

Character Search

Explore a section of your community to investigate local character.

1. Identify the area that you surveyed (e.g., neighborhood, downtown, streets explored). Make a map of the area.

6. What detracts from your community's visual character?

2. Choose five adjectives to describe the appearance of your community.

7. What would you like to change about your community's character?

3. What makes your community unique?

8. Interview community elders, relatives, long-term residents, local architects, contractors, real estate agents, or shop-keepers to gain their insights into how your community's character has changed over time.

4. List five things you see that add to your community's visual character.

9. Optional: Attach any pictures (e.g., photos or sketches) of the area you surveyed.

5. What are the assets in your community?

Natural?	Built?	Historical?	Scenic?	Cultural?

Case Study: Great Smoky Mountain Gateway Communities

Can a community enjoy the benefits of tourism without sacrificing its character?

Located on the boundary of Great Smoky Mountains National Park, Tennessee, the towns of Townsend and Pittman Center have found that uniting residents behind a vision for the future enables them to reap the benefits of tourism without losing what they love about their towns. That approach contrasts sharply with nearby Gatlinburg and Pigeon Forge, where high-powered, high-volume tourism has transformed those two communities into amusement parks.

Gatlinburg and Pigeon Forge

As portals to Great Smoky Mountains National Park, Gatlinburg and Pigeon Forge are perhaps the country's best examples of gateway communities that have been completely transformed by tourism. There are factory outlet stores, wax museums, and T-shirt shops. Go-cart racing is the latest rage; at least 11 ovals are currently available. More adventurous types can visit a vertical wind tunnel that simulates indoor skydiving, play laser tag in a 9,000-square-foot arcade, or jump off a five-story bungee tower. Country music halls and theme parks are very popular.

Gatlinburg (pop. 3,382) and Pigeon Forge (pop. 5,083) exhibit a problem faced by many gateway communities: As the local economy grows increasingly dependent on mass marketing, entertainment, and tourism, the traditional industries and long-time residents are forced out by rising property values and the higher taxes that accompany them. Only a few major landowners have managed to reap big profits from the phenomenal increases in property values. In fact, Gatlinburg no longer has any residential neighborhoods—virtually all housing in the town has been converted to rental property or second homes. Even though both towns now generate an amazing amount of tax revenue, their economies

consist almost entirely of seasonal, low-paying service jobs, not the permanent positions needed to support a family.

Haphazard development of private land in the shadow of the Great Smoky Mountains National Park also takes its toll on the region's magnificent scenery and natural resources. The roads into the Smoky Mountains are lined with bumper-to-bumper traffic and hundreds of billboards. In Gatlinburg, views of the Smokies have been marred by an observation tower, scores of high-rise condominium developments, an aerial tramway, and a 15-story hotel, which, while boasting of its "spectacular views," spoils the view for everyone else.

Worse are the impacts that development has on the park's wildlife—the original attraction for visitors. Every autumn, black bears migrate out of the park in their quest for food to build fat reserves for the long winter. But the rush to find building sites near the park has sealed off important migration corridors that are necessary for the bears to reach feeding grounds, according to Dr. Mike Pelton, a bear biologist at the University of Tennessee. "In the fall, a primary food source for the bears is oak acorns found at lower elevations outside the park," Pelton says. "In real crunch years of scarce food, bears migrating out of the park are getting killed on highways or shot in backyards."

Case Study: Great Smoky Mountain Gateway Communities (cont.)

Can a community bring about change? The Gatlinburg Gateway Foundation was formed in 1998 and developed a vision statement that states, "We are a vibrant community that honors our mountain heritage and embraces our responsibility as the gateway to Great Smoky Mountains National Park." Over several years of community meetings and open dialogue, positive changes have been influenced and the community has crafted a future vision which has helped shape its character and develop a sense of place.

Change has started. Gatlinburg is now erasing its mistakes and changing its character. They are under grounding power lines to have a better view of the mountains, developing architectural guidelines for businesses to blend better with the mountainscape, and giving aesthetic facelifts to old buildings. They are also working to bring the arts and crafts community downtown, and building on heritage tourism opportunities. They have created the Gatlinburg Partnership Council that brings together key community groups and citizens to find solutions to problems and to better plan for the future. Although Pigeon Forge does not have the organized energy of Gatlinburg, they too are trying to develop events that are more in keeping with their gateway responsibility. For further information on these changes visit www.gatlinburggateway.com

Townsend

Fifteen miles south of Gatlinburg is Townsend (pop. 244), another town bordering on the park. Positioning itself as an alternative to the glitter of its neighbors, Townsend has adopted the slogan "The peaceful side of the Smokies." The town's appeal lies not in bungee jumping, go-cart racing, or factory outlets, but in its natural amenities: cool, clear rivers for fishing and floating; family-owned and operated lodges; a colorful history; scenic trails and country roads for hiking, biking, and horseback riding; and a chance to see a black bear or a white-tailed deer in the wild.

"Most of the people here don't want Townsend to become like Gatlinburg," says City Councilwoman Sandy Headrick. "We don't want to live in a town with traffic jams and Dollywoods and water slides."

Pittman Center

Just north of Gatlinburg is the small town of Pittman Center (pop. 477), which also has successfully preserved its character. In 1989, Pittman Center residents convened a series of public meetings designed to produce a shared vision for their future. They decided to prohibit billboards and garish signs, limit commercial development to the town's core, and protect the flow and quality of the Little Pigeon River, which runs through town.

To realize this vision, Pittman Center enacted several widely supported ordinances. One limits development of hillsides and steep slopes. "We've tried to recognize that real estate which is hard to develop shouldn't be developed," says Jim Coykendall, an architect who has lived in Pittman Center since 1969.

Another ordinance places size limits on signs and prohibits billboards so that the community's streets and highways remain uncluttered. Leading by example, Pittman Center's street

Case Study: Great Smoky Mountain Gateway Communities (cont.)

signs are made of wood rather than metal. And the first thing visitors see is an attractive wooden sign that reads "Pittman Center—A Community Dedicated to Preserving Our Mountain Heritage."

Coykendall attributes Pittman Center's success not only to the public's involvement in the visioning process, but also to the local people who have made sure the community follows up on its ideas. "If you can get just four or five people to commit the time and the effort, they can bring the rest of the community along," he says. "You can always get outside assistance, but the process has got to be driven from inside the community."

Can places such as Townsend and Pittman Center preserve their unique qualities and still enjoy a healthy economy? According to Townsend's Sandy Headrick, the answer is a resounding "yes." "There's a lot of room for controlled growth," she says. "We think we can have a good business sector and still maintain the peace and quiet that we have here now."

Source:
J. Howe, E. McMahon, and L. Propst; *Balancing Nature and Commerce in Gateway Communities*, Washington, DC: Island Press, 1997, 32–36. Adapted and reprinted with permission from Island Press.

Questions to Consider:

1. Which towns would you want to visit? Why?

2. Which towns would you want to live in? Why?

3. What are the land use issues?

4. What are some possible outcomes?

5. How does visual pollution affect a community's character? What else affects its character?

6. How can the residents of the different communities preserve their local character?

7. What lessons are to be learned from Gatlinburg as the community now tries to change some of their past development?

Case Study: Local Land Use Issue

Student Group Members:

_____

_____

_____

_____

1. What is the land use issue in your community that your group selected?

2. What area is affected by this issue (for example, block, neighborhood, city, county, watershed)?

3. Who are the "players," and what are their positions?

4. What are the values and beliefs of the players?

5. Who or what else might be affected by this issue?

6. What local laws are connected to this issue?

7. What are the possible solutions?

8. What solution do you recommend?

9. If your recommended solution were used, what possible effects would it have on the following:

   • Environment?

   • Local citizens?

   • Economy?

   • Community character?

10. According to the effects above, what should be done to resolve the issue? Why?

11. How does this issue affect your sense of place?

Case Study: Dudley Street Neighborhood Initiative

What drives the remarkable scale of change here? Resident voices determine how their dream of an urban village unfolds. And at the center of this renaissance have been young people who, nurtured by adults who believe in them, have contributed guts, ambition and sincerity to building their community.

—**"Essential Partners," report for the Annie E. Casey Foundation**

Since 1985, the residents of the Dudley Street neighborhood have been working together to revitalize their community. Located less than two miles from downtown Boston, Massachusetts, the Dudley Street neighborhood suffered from arson, illegal dumping, lack of investing, neglect, and illegal practices by banks and other lending institutions of denying loans or restricting the number of loans for certain areas of a community (called "redlining").

Although one of the poorest neighborhoods in Boston (the per capita income is half that of the city of Boston), the Dudley Street neighborhood is rich in ethnic diversity. Community members are African American, Latino, Cape Verdean, and Caucasian. Those residents decided to take matters into their own hands, forming the Dudley Street Neighborhood Initiative (DSNI). DSNI is a nonprofit community-based planning and organizing entity that works to implement resident-driven plans for revitalizing the area. Since its formation in the mid-1980s, DSNI has grown into a collaborative effort of more than 2,700 resident members, businesses, nonprofit organizations, and religious institutions that are concerned with revitalizing this culturally diverse neighborhood of 24,000 people and rediscovering its character and affordability.

DSNI's major accomplishment has been—and continues to be—organizing and empowering the residents of the Dudley Street neighborhood to create a shared vision of that area. The residents make this vision a reality by creating strategic partnerships with individuals and organizations in the private, government, and nonprofit sectors. For example, in 1986, DSNI's first community-wide campaign, "Don't Dump on Us," was victorious in getting the city to clean up vacant lots and to tow abandoned cars. In 1987, that same campaign was successful in closing illegal trash transfer stations and restoring commuter rail service. And in 1991, the "Dudley Pride" campaign kicked off with trash barrels placed along Dudley Street.

The youth in the community are just as involved in the revitalization process as the adults, working with other community members to reestablish their neighborhood's character. In 1990, architects and planners worked with more than 40 youths to plan and design community centers. In 1993, the community's youths designed and painted Unity Mural. And in 1994, the Youth Landscape Training Project upgraded lots on Dennis Street.

The DSNI continues to grow and have an impact on the community. The membership has grown to 3,670. Many of the children who were residents of the area when DSNI started are now the leaders of the organization today. More than 600 of the 1300 vacant lots have been rehabilitated for homes, gardens, parks, and playgrounds. The Vine Street Community Center was constructed and recently opened serving the community in a variety of ways. In 2004, *Celebrate Boston* held the kickoff event to the Democratic National Convention at the DSNI offices to recognize the innovative achievements of the organization.

Sources:
Benfield, Terris, and Vorsanger 2001, 34–40 (A)
"Dudley Street Neighborhood Initiative," 2004 (E).
DSNI Historic Timeline," 2002 (E)
The Dudley Street Neighborhood Initiative, 2004 (E)

Notes

Mapping Your Community Through Time

Student teams investigate the social, cultural, economic, aesthetic, and environmental components of their community to create map overlays and reports describing the development of their community through time.

Subjects
Drafting, Earth Science, Economics, Environmental Science, Geography, Government, and Social Studies.

Concepts
2.10 Cultural and societal perspectives influence the attitudes, beliefs, and biases of people toward the use of resources and environmental protection.

4.6 Human-built environments, if planned, constructed, and landscaped to be compatible with the environment in which they will be located, can conserve resources, enhance environmental quality, and promote the comfort and well-being of those who will live within them.

5.4 Ecosystems change over time through patterns of growth and succession. They are also affected by other phenomena such as disease, insects, fire, weather, climate, and human intervention.

Skills
Analyzing, Comparing and Contrasting, Discussing, Formulating Questions, Inferring, Interpreting, Observing, Ordering and Arranging, Researching

Materials
Overhead transparencies; fine-point colored erasable and permanent pens; cardboard; thumbtacks or pushpins; copies of student pages; aerial photographs and maps of your community. Optional: GIS data layers, computers, GIS software, Internet access.

Time Considerations
Five 50-minute periods

Objectives
▶ Students will research the social, cultural, economic, aesthetic, and environmental components of their community in different time periods.

▶ Students will transfer their research information to map layers and interpret their findings.

▶ Students will gain insight into Geographic Information Systems (GIS) mapping technology and about the power of maps to analyze and present information.

▶ Students will explore how or if their own sense of place is influenced by their community's history.

Assessments
▶ Have students create several map layers for the block where they live (or if they live in a more rural area, they can show the general area around their home). This exercise allows them to choose the characteristics to depict. Students can present their maps and can explain why they chose the different features and how those features might relate to their sense of place.

▶ Challenge students to imagine the future of their community on the basis of the trends they discovered in their research. For example, if green space is disappearing, how much longer will there still be green areas in your community? How might such trends affect the community's visual character? Have students discuss what they foresee as the greatest challenges for the future of their community.

Background

The history of a place fortifies the context and strengthens the relevance of what students experience. If they can see themselves as part of a continuous line from the past to the present, they will be able to visualize and value their role in the future.

—Matt Sanger (B)

What do photographs, interviews, essays, articles, books, movies, and maps have in common? They can all be used to tell the story of a place. Maps are powerful tools that can display characteristics of a place at a moment in time, or they can reveal change over time. By comparing maps from different periods, we can unveil the history and stories of a place, as well as make predictions about the future.

What Are Maps?

A map is a picture of a place, usually from directly above, with distances, directions, and scale accurately depicted.[1] See the student page titled "Maps and Map Features" for definitions and further information. Maps are graphic representations that can be used to illustrate selected physical, cultural, or social aspects occurring on the Earth. Maps can visually represent information ranging from landforms and bodies of water to streets, buildings, and sewer systems. They can also represent abstract information such as population density, percentage of urbanization, or ethnic diversity. A map can be a simple line drawing on paper illustrating

directions from one place to another or a computer-generated, three-dimensional color map depicting a region's topography.[2]

Normally when we look at the world from ground level, we don't see much of it from any one spot. If we were to stand on a sidewalk, for example, we might see several buildings, a strip of road, and a couple of green trees, but our view is generally quite limited. From above, however, places look radically different. By looking at larger pieces of the world from above, we can see the relationship of one point to another—the orientation of the buildings to the rest of the block or of the block to the rest of the neighborhood or city.[3]

Analyzing such relationships is useful for determining the patterns formed by the placement of either physical or abstract features on the Earth's surface. Those arrangements can be explored, organized, and analyzed, thereby allowing investigators to generate hypotheses about the causes of such patterns. Hypotheses can also be formed about abstract features, such as the flow of trade or extent of political influence. Those hypotheses are then applied to a multitude of disciplines, such as regional planning, historical documentation, or property assessment.[4] Looking at the "big picture" greatly improves our ability to analyze situations and spatial distribution before we make decisions, whether we're charting the fastest route to school or shaping the future of our communities.

What Is GIS?

A *Geographic Information System* (GIS) connects maps and data, leading to maps that offer an opportunity to examine spatial relationships. A GIS is a combination of elements designed to store, retrieve, manipulate, and display information about places—which together are known as geographic data. It is a package consisting of four basic parts: robust hardware, powerful software, spatial data, and a critical thinker.[5] A GIS manages location-based information in data layers—one layer for each characteristic such as population characteristics, economic development opportunities, or vegetation types—and provides the tools to overlay, display, and analyze the information contained in those data layers.

How does GIS work? First, geographic information must be gathered. Often, this compilation is done with Global Positioning System (GPS) receivers, which determine the latitude and longitude of a point or boundary of a particular location. This information is transported between GPS satellites (there are 24 orbiting the Earth at a given time) and the receiver. Once gathered, the information is downloaded to the GIS software and is used to create maps. Sometimes, this information can be downloaded from different organizations, including the U.S. Census Bureau.

GIS software takes numbers and words from the columns and rows in a database and plots them on a map by tying each piece of data in a data layer to a specific location. Transforming data into a map format helps reveal patterns

that we may not see otherwise.[6] A growing number of professionals and industries are using GIS applications, including the following:[7]

- Marine biologists, terrestrial ecologists, botanists, foresters, and wildlife and natural resource managers use GIS to analyze, interpret, and present biological data.
- Transportation planners use GIS to monitor mass transit systems or map highway systems or to track shipping vessels.
- Telecommunications specialists use GIS for network planning, customer relations, and marketing strategies.
- Real estate agents and market analysts use GIS to examine housing values and trends.

Another application for GIS is exploring history. Mapping the past with GIS is a relatively new field. Historians and archaeologists are finding GIS technology easier to use than ever and are pushing the boundaries of GIS, applying it in new and creative ways. For example, in the Andes Mountains, people who had hunted and gathered wild foods for thousands of years eventually settled down, domesticated llamas and alpacas, and built empires. Archeologists painstakingly explore this transition by excavating large areas and recording their findings in minute detail. GIS provides the researchers with a powerful tool to document, organize, and display their excavations and findings.[8]

Why Use GIS?

[We use GIS] to be a positive force in society—to make well-considered decisions, to be a resource with the potential to improve the quality of life—people need to be comfortable with exploring and integrating information, seeking relationships, thinking critically, acknowledging differences, and finding common ground.

—Environmental Systems Research Institute (C)

GIS technology is bringing new perspectives and views of the world into education and is bridging the gap between indoor and outdoor classrooms. For instance, as part of an outdoor ecology lesson, students might use magnifying glasses to take a closer look at the leaves of a particular tree. Today, technology education offers the opportunity to reverse that perspective, taking a closer look from afar. After measuring the number of trees in a small forest plot, students can access a satellite image of the entire forest or can translate their hard data into spatial data, thereby making the connection between their firsthand experience and what they learn from a distance.[9]

Students who have some familiarity with [GIS] technology will be better able to influence the direction of future ecological research and to ensure that rational decisions are made about the use of environmental resources.

— Robert L. Friedrich and Robert V. Blystone (C)

Physical Components of Your Community

What components shape the design and function of our communities? Some of the key building blocks are housing, **zoning**, public infrastructure (e.g., roads, transportation, sewer and water lines, schools, hospitals, courthouses), **green infrastructure** (e.g., **open spaces**, rivers, mountains), businesses, and industries. Together, those components help create the physical and visual framework of our communities. None of the components exist in a vacuum; rather, they are intimately linked to the social, economic, cultural, and political fabric of a community. Furthermore, none of the components are static—our communities are constantly changing and growing.

Examining changes to physical components over time can provide insight into accompanying developments. For example, growing numbers of houses and schools usually indicate population growth. New developments might lead to expanding sewer lines and the disruption of natural habitat. An explosion of new businesses usually indicates economic growth. Looking at the interplay between different components, such as transportation and industry, can also reveal important information about a community, such as growth patterns or interdependencies between the building blocks. And in some cases, studying and comparing maps can reveal patterns or issues that might otherwise escape unnoticed. For example, it might be difficult to realize changes in green space until visual maps are compared. Most of us find it easier to understand patterns and changes through visual representations rather than through numbers, tables, and anecdotal observations.

Mapping Your Community

GIS can be a powerful tool to explore the history of our own communities. In the activities that follow, students can use one of two methods for creating their own set of map layers for their community. If your students have access to computers with Internet access (preferably high-speed access), they can use maps available online to obtain data layers. However, the use of computers is entirely optional (although we recommend encouraging your students to explore at least some of the GIS resources that are available online). As a second option, students can create a simulated GIS by creating and overlaying overhead transparencies to learn more about their local area. Even if students don't have a chance to use computers, they will gain an understanding of how GIS works and will discover how maps can be used to track and illuminate community changes over time.

To develop their maps, students will need to draw on community resources, such as historic maps, town offices, libraries, and residents. Depending on your situation, you might consider doing some of the legwork ahead of time. For more information on finding maps and data for your community, please see Appendix C.

Endnotes

1 U.S. Geological Survey 2002 (E).
2 National Geographic Research and Exploration 1994 (D).
3 U.S. Geological Survey 2002 (E).
4 Campbell 2001 (A).
5 Environmental Systems Research Institute 1998 (C).
6 Malone, Palmer, and Voigt 2002 (D).
7 Environmental Systems Research Institute 2003 (E).
8 Haskin 2002 (C).
9 Haskin 2002 (C).

Letters following author and date citations refer to sections in the bibliography (Appendix B) where the reader can find full data about the sources cited.

Getting Ready

- Gather GIS data layers or overhead transparencies; fine-point erasable and permanent pens in various colors for writing on overheads; cardboard; and thumbtacks or pushpins. Essentially, the layers of the overheads will form a low-tech Geographic Information System.
- See Appendix C and the student page titled "Maps and Map Features" for more information on mapping.
- Photocopy the six "Team" student pages (one for each team) and, if you choose, the optional student pages titled "Research Hints," "Maps and Map Features," and the "Case Study."
- *Base Map*: Create an 8.5" x 11" base map. You might copy an existing map or select parts of different maps to draw your own base map. The key to creating or choosing the base map is to provide enough detail so that students can stay oriented, but not so much information that it will clutter the map or take away from the teams' projects. Include latitude, longitude, a legend, a scale,

and a north arrow on your base map. As resources, consider street maps, topographic maps, **planimetric maps**, and aerial views of your community (see Appendix C for tips on where to find maps). The U.S. Census Bureau's website (www.census.gov) is one good resource for creating your base map. Visit the online mapping section and use the TIGER map server. You can select the scale and the data layers that you want to include (e.g., latitude and longitude, waterways, streets, railroads, parks). Many of the online mapping resources offer the opportunity to zoom in and out as desired. If you choose to draw your own map, you might include only a few select features, such as local waterways and a grid including some of the main streets—just enough to orient students. After you finish creating your base map, make copies for all students.

- *Aerial Photograph*: Find at least one aerial photograph of your community. (Community changes will be more apparent if more aerial photographs are collected.) See Appendix C for tips on finding aerial photos.
- *Thematic Maps*: As mentioned above, the U.S. Census Bureau is a great source of ready-made thematic maps that illustrate characteristics of your community. Try printing out a few sample thematic maps to share with your students. If you have trouble printing or photocopying a clear map, consider showing the maps on a computer. As another option, try to find hard-copy maps (e.g., road maps, green maps, topographic maps) illustrating different themes.
- Consider accumulating research materials for the teams in advance.
- If you live in an agricultural area, consider having one team research and map agricultural patterns over time for the activity that follows.
- *Optional*: Approach the school or the public library about letting the students add a book of maps with accompanying research about their community to the archives. Or contact the historical society to ask if the students could submit their work to the archives. The students' maps can also be displayed at parent–teacher conferences, school events, or community fairs.

Doing the Activity

1. Brainstorm ways the local community has changed over time. Ask students the following questions: Is your community different today from when you were younger? What changes have you observed? (Tell them to consider roads, retail stores, playing fields, open spaces, natural areas, housing developments, and other components.)

2. Discuss the definition of **community**, mentioning that a community can be defined at different scales. Remind students that a community is a group of individuals and elements coexisting and interacting dynamically. Communities include living and nonliving components such as animals, plants, humans, waterways, and buildings. To help students visualize their community, show an aerial photograph of your area. If you are unable to obtain an aerial photo, show a map of the school district or local roads. Ask students if they think the map would look the same 10 years ago or 10 years in the future. What might be similar? Different?

3. Share sample thematic maps with your students to illustrate characteristics of your community (see "Getting Ready" for details). As another option to motivate your students, encourage them to explore online or paper maps on their own (see the "Enrichment" section for more ideas). Discuss GIS technology and the power of maps to bring concepts to life. Again, ask students how the maps might change over time. What might be similar or different? How is your community changing? *Optional*: If your students have had little access to maps, perhaps have them first create a map of where they live or have them identify scale, orientation, and different symbols on a map. The following resources provide more information on maps and on using maps with students: Mark Monmonier, *How to Lie with Maps* (Chicago: University of Chicago Press, 1996); Roger Hart, *Children's Participation* (London: Earthscan Publications, 1997.)

4. Explain that students will be studying physical elements of the local community over time, and share with them an overview of the project (see below). *Note*: As a technology extension, consider having your students create computerized maps as opposed to hard-copy maps on overhead transparencies. To showcase their results, you can display students' maps on a screen using a LCD projector.

Overview of Project

- Collectively, the class will create a series of map overlays on overhead transparancies and complementary reports that depict different aspects of the local community and show how it has changed over time.
- The class will be divided into teams by topic: zoning, water, transportation, and so forth.
- Within each team, different people will be responsible for researching and mapping different time periods: early 1900s, 1950s, 1990s, and today.
- All maps will be created by using the same reference base map. All teams will use the same scale for their maps and the same latitude and longitude, so that any map can be placed over any other map.
- Each team will create a work plan with specific tasks and will submit it for feedback.
- The final maps and background reports will be bound into a reference book.

5. *Optional*: Share the case study titled "Developing San Antonio's 'Broadway Corridor'" to help students get a feel for how GIS and mapping are used to make decisions. For an online example, have students visit www.hillsboroughcounty.org.

6. Divide the class into six teams. Each team should have at least four students; if you have a small class, consider reducing the number of time periods for research or omitting a topic. Assign teams to the different topics listed below. Hand out the appropriate "Team Objective" student page for each team, which describes the teams' tasks and suggests helpful resources. Also consider distributing a copy of the optional "Research Hints" student page to each student (or you might prefer to have the research component be more student guided).

Team Topics

- Zoning and Regulations
- Housing
- Transportation
- Water and Wastewater
- Green Infrastructure
- Business and Industry

7. Give each student a copy of the base map. Review it together and make sure everyone understands the geography. You may want students to identify latitude, longitude, direction, and scale. Mention that tips for drawing the team maps can be found at the bottom of "Research Hints."

8. Briefly discuss some of the different types of maps that students might find in their research. Aerial photos, planimetrics, topographic maps, and others are explained on the student page "Maps and Map Features."

9. Challenge students to use the next 30 minutes to plan who will research and map which aspects of the topic and how. Teams will need to submit their work plans to you by the end of class. To help guide students, consider reading aloud the following sample plan from a Green Infrastructure Team:

"The Green Infrastructure Team will map forested areas, parks, and open space at 30-year intervals. Each person on our team will research what the state of green infrastructure is in his or her time period, what decisions were made, and what the decisions indicated about the values of the time regarding land use.

The research will be written up, combined, edited, and then typed into a final team report for the "Green Infrastructure" chapter. Each person will also create a map overlay of the green infrastructure for his or her time period using the agreed-upon symbols. We will include photographs of open space, parks, and the forest as it appears today, plus the types of trees in our community. We also hope to find old photos.

One student will interview a natural resource professional (e.g., forester, biologist, arborist, or farmer). The second student will conduct an online search for aerial photographs of the community over time and will contact the mapping department in City Hall for more information. A third student will conduct interviews in the community, and our fourth team member will support the other three as needed, including compiling the bibliography and typing. Supplies needed: overhead sheets and transparency markers."

10. To check students' comprehension of tasks, present the following prompt and ask students to submit their response in writing at the next class: Summarize what you already know about your topic. Record three questions you will research, and explain how you will gather the information.

11. The next day, have students gather into teams by topic. Return the teams' work plans to them to review. At this point, teams are ready to launch into independent research. If it is not feasible for students to go to the library, you can gather reference materials in advance in the classroom. Assist students with calls to municipal offices, local museums, or historical societies to establish contacts and to set up meeting times. (Students can also use e-mail to establish contact.) Periodically check in with each team.

12. Divide students into teams according to their assigned time periods (1900s, 1950s, 1990s, and today). Those students planning to interview an older person might team up or carpool and ask the interviewee about two or three different topics. Encourage students researching similar time periods to share historical reference materials.

13. Instruct students to continue their independent research and to begin writing up and mapping their findings. Emphasize the need to credit all sources in the bibliography. Because this is a historical research project, students are not expected to create content. Students should keep this objective in mind as they write.

14. Remind students to complete their interviews, write-ups, and maps as ongoing homework.

15. Gather students into teams by topic to present their maps and research. Use an overhead projector, which will allow each team to show the changes in their topic by overlaying the maps according to time period. As each team presents its research, discuss the following questions:
- What trends are visible?
- What was happening in the community, the county, the state, and the world that contributed to those changes?
- If we consider those trends, what might we predict about the future?
- How else might the maps be layered to discover more information?
- Can you find any relationships between the maps used by the different teams? (Try overlapping different maps from other teams for the same time period.)
- What do you find surprising?
- What else do you want to know?
- How else can you use GIS to explore your community?

16. Edit, bind, and submit the final written work to the school library, local planning department, or local historical society.

17. Debrief the activity by discussing students' discoveries about their community, other questions raised by the exercise, benefits of mapping, and whether this new knowledge affects their sense of place.

Enrichment

- Encourage your students to practice using real GIS technology online. Starting with the following websites, students can explore on their own or can conduct a class demonstration.
  - The Environmental Systems Research Institute Inc. (ESRI) is a source of GIS resources, software, and data. ESRI also offers free "lightweight" GIS software on its website, www.esri.com. Download or use the computerized mapping software online to provide your students with a great opportunity to explore real GIS technology.
  - The U.S. Environmental Protection Agency (www.epa.gov) also offers resources for exploring GIS and learning more about your local community plus other parts of the country. Visit www.epa.gov/myenvironment, to explore live maps about the environmental conditions in your area.
  - Visit the U.S. Geological Survey's website (www.usgs.gov), where students can make maps using the National Atlas, which is designed to stimulate children and adults to visualize and understand complex relationships between environments, places, and people. Making maps allows students to explore environmental, demographic, economic, social, political, and historical dimensions of American life.

- The Green Map System (www.greenmap.com) is a resource for students interested in mapping the connections between their natural and **built environments**.
  - As mentioned in the "Getting Ready" section, users can select data layers and can customize maps at the U.S. Census Bureau's website: www.census.gov.
- Invite students to find information and ready-made maps online that provide more information about your local community. Following is a short list of sources for local information (see Appendix C for more ideas):
  - The U.S. Census Bureau (www.census.gov), as mentioned earlier, offers a wealth of population, housing, economic, and geographic information based on census data, including an array of thematic maps.
  - Also mentioned earlier, the U.S. Environmental Protection Agency (www.epa.gov) offers extensive environmental information about your community. For example, students can use the EnviroMapper function, surf their watershed, explore air quality, and learn what is being done locally to protect the environment.
  - At the Environmental Defense Fund Scorecard site (www.scorecard.org), you can enter your zipcode to access plenty of information about the environmental health of your community.
- Use the video *Making Sense of Place - Phoenix: The Urban Desert*, a one-hour documentary film about Phoenix, Arizona which has expanded from a small desert town to the sixth largest city in the United States in just 50 years. The film explores the interrelationships both caused by and affecting individual choices, the democratic process and market forces in the region. For further information visit www.makingsenseofplace.com.

Research Hints

- Think about which of the resources listed below might be helpful for your team. You'll also find more specific suggestions on each "Team" page.

  - Libraries (town or city, school, or university)
  - Local historical society
  - Historic preservation team
  - Town or city planning department or engineering services offices
  - Local or regional planning committee or planning district commission
  - Other government offices, especially land management offices (Check your local phone book for ideas.)
  - U.S. Census Bureau (www.census.gov)
  - Internet (You're more likely to find recent resources online.)
  - Community residents, town officials, and professionals
  - Museums
  - Environmental organizations
  - Land trust
  - Fire insurance atlases
  - American Planning Association (www.planning.org)
  - Planning department at the state university

- Explore your community and see what you can discover. For example, can you find old rail tracks? Homes under construction or abandoned buildings? Do civic buildings have plaques with dates? Are there overgrown areas that once thrived? Old tree stumps?

- Whom might you interview? Town or county employees, neighbors, professionals, and elders might have insight into your topic. Elders in your community can be a great source of historical information. Try contacting a local retirement center or the Rotary or Elks club. Call and ask to interview a "local," someone who grew up in the area. When you make a call as part of your research, first introduce yourself and the project, and then ask if someone might be able to help you learn more. If possible, schedule a meeting

with your contact and explain your project in more detail. Come to the meeting with questions already prepared. Perhaps you might even want to send your questions to the interviewee. Listen carefully and take notes or use a recorder (ask first). Some people will be very uncomfortable with a recorder running—weigh the advantages. Send a thank you card or a copy of the project as a follow-up.

- Try to find information as close to your assigned time period as possible. However, you may need to be flexible to accommodate the resources you can find.

- Some information may be available in ready-made map format. In other cases, you might need to study data and tables or to read text to learn more.

Tips for Drawing Maps

- Remember to refer to the base map when you draw your maps! All maps need to be drawn using the same coordinates and scale, and they should line up when placed on top of each other.

- Draw only the elements directly related to your topic. For example, the Green Infrastructure Team should only draw vegetation. The Zoning and Regulations Team will provide the buildings necessary to see how green space has changed.

- Create a rough draft of your map first.

Maps and Map Features

Two of the most useful resources to lend a new perspective on your community are planimetric maps and aerial photographs. **Planimetric maps** (or just "planimetrics") are maps that show line drawings of ground features. For example, a planimetric map might show building outlines, edges of roadways, sidewalks, tree lines, bodies of water, manhole covers, fire hydrants, and other similar objects. A planimetric map does not usually contain elevation data. (**Topographic maps**, however, are designed to show elevation; they are made up of a system of lines to illustrate the "lay of the land." Topographic maps can be an important source of information, but they may be a bit cluttered for use in the following activities.) Comparing planimetric maps can be one of the best ways to track changes in your community over time. Planimetric maps, which are usually drawn at a scale of 1 inch to 100 feet, can be obtained in the survey and mapping department of a municipality or at the city or county engineer's office.

Aerial photographs are excellent tools to show the elements of your community. Unlike maps, which usually highlight a theme (such as roads) and de-emphasize or exclude other components of the community, aerial photographs offer an unbiased snapshot. If available from different time periods, aerial photographs also offer an excellent opportunity to track community change over time. An aerial photograph will not, however, reveal hidden elements (such as sewer lines) or artificial distinctions (such as zoning areas).

All maps have certain elements. A **title** should indicate the purpose or subject of the map, the time period it represents, and any other relevant information.

Scale is a crucial element to all maps. Scale lets a person know the ratio between the distance of features on the map and the distance of those same features on Earth. This ratio can be expressed in several ways, including a word statement, ratio, fraction, or graphic scale. Here are some examples of the ways to express scale. The

methods of illustrating scale are different, but the actual value of the measure remains the same.

1 inch to 1 mile
1:63,360 (Read "1 inch equals 63,360 inches" [or 1 mile]; the unit of measure is constant.)
1/63,360 (Again, the unit must remain constant.)

This device allows the map user to measure distance on the map and then to translate the measurement to the distance on the ground. In this case, 1 inch equals 1 mile.)

Legends show map symbols (such as lines, circles, or other shapes and any corresponding colors) and explain what they represent (such as roads, trees, or cities).

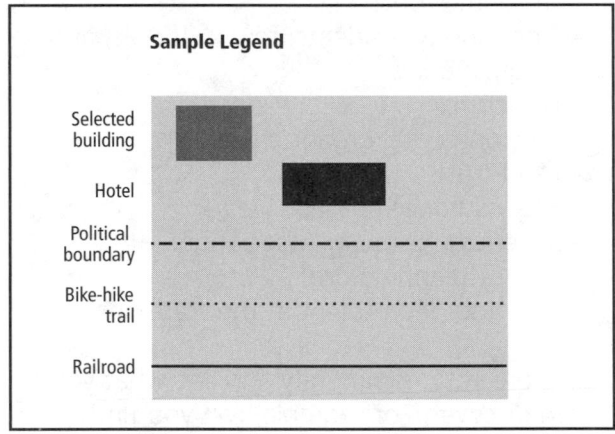

The map should also include the names of any displayed political or physical **features** and a reference to the source where the information was gathered.

Orientation informs the map user of the map's alignment relative to the Earth's surface. Although most maps are oriented with north at the top of the map, this direction isn't always true. Therefore, a map will usually contain a north arrow.

Source:
John Campbell, *Map Use and Analysis*, 4th ed. (New York: McGraw-Hill, 2001).

Team—Zoning and Regulations

Zoning defines how a given area will be used by establishing a range of acceptable development options for a piece of property according to a classification of land uses. There are both single- and mixed-use zones. Land use generally includes office, commercial, industrial, residential, agricultural, recreational, conservation, and scenic categories, but the exact names and classifications can vary by community. Once established by officials in the local government, the land uses are identified on a zoning map and are further defined in a zoning ordinance (the set of laws that manages zoning). Zoning maps are available from a town or city's planning department.

Your team is responsible for mapping civic buildings such as libraries, schools, museums, courthouses, post offices, recreation centers, and other government buildings.

Objectives

1. Describe the plans and regulations that guided the development of your community over time. Study zoning regulations in your area. When were zoning regulations first introduced? Why were zoning codes developed?

2. Map the municipal structures and public facilities (excluding mass transit and roads) that define your town or city, as well as the different zoning designations for the following time periods:
- Early 1900s
- 1950s
- 1990s
- Today

Resources

To learn more about zoning in your community, contact the zoning and planning department for your town or city (or county). Other helpful sources for your team are the town hall, local library, historical societies, board of education, phone books, tourist and welcome centers, personal observations, and the Internet.

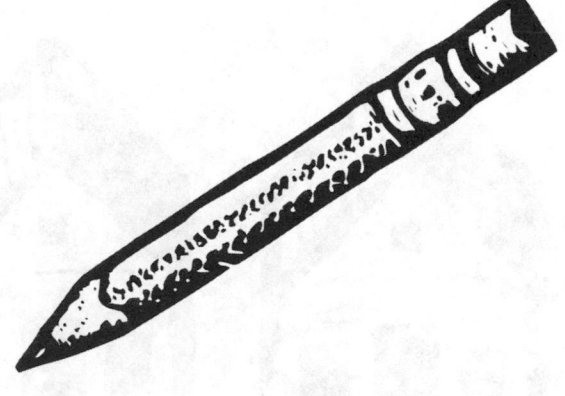

Team—Housing

A housing unit is a structure designated as living quarters. It can be a house, apartment, mobile home, condominium complex, nursing home, or retirement community. Zoning regulations often determine minimum and maximum lot and home sizes.

Objective

Describe and map the spread of housing through your community over the following time periods:

• Early 1900s
• 1950s
• 1990s
• Today

Resources

Good starter resources for your topic are the U.S. Census Bureau's website (www.census.gov), your town or city planning offices, the community housing department, the Internet, and the tax office. Walk around your community to see what you discover. What other resources can you find?

Team—Transportation

Transportation is how we move people and goods from one place to another. Modes of transportation can vary from automobiles to airplanes, bicycles to boats, and trains to trucks. Any mode of transportation requires a system of infrastructure to function (e.g., local roads, highways, ports, paths, airports, parking lots).

Objective

Research and map the use of transportation (e.g., roadways, train tracks, bus routes, airports, parking lots) in your community over the following time periods:
- Early 1900s
- 1950s
- 1990s
- Today

Resources

Your team might contact your local government's street, highway, and transit departments; government planning offices; bicycle, pedestrian, and transit advocacy groups; transportation companies; and transportation hubs for information. See what other resources you can find. Can you locate old schedules and route maps? Also think about libraries, historical resources, and the Internet. Does your community have master street plans and bikeway plans? Walk around your community and make observations. Where did abandoned railways once go, and who used them? What preceded today's high-speed rails—a wagon track? Has the availability of transit changed?

Team—Water and Wastewater

When you turn on the faucet, where does the water come from? Some people draw their water from individual wells, deep holes dug into the ground to obtain water. Others rely on water piped in from reservoirs or aquifers that are miles away. What water systems are in place to provide water for the residents in your community? How have the systems changed over time?

In most urban and suburban communities, where people live close together, a sewage system directs, collects, and treats the wastewater that is created when we flush the toilet, take a shower, and pour things down the drain. A typical sewage system is made up of pipes that connect individual houses and buildings to larger pipes that lead to a wastewater treatment plant. In many rural communities where people live farther apart, individuals have their own sewage treatment plants, called septic tanks. Other areas now use holding tanks, which require periodic pumping.

Objective

Describe the methods of distributing clean water and controlling the flow of wastewater in your community over the following time periods:
- Early 1900s
- 1950s
- 1990s
- Today

Resources

Your team might want to contact your town or city government's planning offices, water department, or sewage treatment plants for more information. Sewer and water maps may be available from the engineer's office or public utilities departments in your town or city. If you are investigating septic systems, contact your local government offices. Also think about using libraries, the Internet, and historical resources. What other sources can you find?

Team—Green Infrastructure

Green infrastructure is the planet's natural life support system—a strategically planned and managed network of wilderness, parks, greenways, conservation easements, and working lands with conservation value. This land supports native species, maintains natural ecological processes, sustains air and water resources, and contributes to the health and quality of life for America's communities and people. When we think of infrastructure, we usually think of built infrastructure such as roads, electric power lines, and water systems, as well as social infrastructure such as schools, hospitals, and libraries. Visit http://greeninfrastructure.net for more information.

Objective

Research the geographic distribution of your community's green infrastructure over the following time periods:

- Early 1900s
- 1950s
- 1990s
- Today

Resources

Your team might want to contact the town or city planning offices, Bureau of Land Management district offices, park and forestry departments, historical societies, environmental groups, soil and water conservation departments, and community conservation organizations. See what kinds of maps, books, and recreation tips you can find in libraries or online. Aerial photos can help give a sense of your community's green infrastructure. Explore your community and see what you discover. Think about how changes in your community's green infrastructure affect its visual character. Look at newly developed areas. What was there before the development? What other resources can you find?

Team—Business and Industry

The economic viability of a community is closely tied to the businesses and industries in the area. Sometimes, it is the industry that brings viability to the community, and sometimes, it is the other way around. The location of commercial and industrial development is related to zoning regulations.

Objective

Research, map, and report on the businesses and industries that exist or once existed in your community over the following time periods:

• Early 1900s
• 1950s
• 1990s
• Today

Resources

To learn more about business and industry in your community, explore historical resources, libraries, small business associations, chambers of commerce, phone books, town planning departments, and tax offices. Other helpful sources of information are the town hall and the Internet.

Case Study: Developing San Antonio's "Broadway Corridor"

by Lance Freeman and Eliot Allen

San Antonio, Texas is widely known for its successful downtown development that brings seven million visitors annually to attractions such as the Alamo and River Walk. Four miles long, the Broadway Corridor is currently home to 12,000 residents and 13,000 workers. The area enjoys an extraordinary collection of community assets, including the local zoo, botanical gardens, two museums, and a university. It also has more than 140 acres of vacant land and dozens of redevelopable properties, making it attractive for infill and economic growth.

The planning effort is distinguished by the way in which GIS brought diverse interests together to work collaboratively on a common vision for the area. In recent years, several community groups were independently looking at problems and opportunities along the Corridor. Instead, they are now jointly using GIS to find common ground. The following are examples of shareholder interests:

- A local group of architects designed an evaluation that was prompted by the Corridor's valuable inventory of redevelopable and historic buildings that could be reached by an extension of the River Walk.
- The city planning department saw the Corridor as an ideal location for testing the "smart growth" provisions of its new uniform development code that encourages redevelopment of established neighborhoods.
- Because Broadway Avenue has unused traffic capacity, the city public works department was interested in multimodal transportation improvements to encourage walking, biking, and transit. Additional transit use was also the goal of VIA Metropolitan Transit, the local transit operator whose goal is increasing ridership while supporting economic growth.
- The Alamo Area Council of Governments, in its capacity as the regional data center, saw the project as an opportunity to better define interactions between land use, transportation, and the environment.

The catalyst for bringing those shareholders together was an offer from the U.S. Environmental Protection Agency (EPA) to apply Smart Growth INDEX, a GIS-based planning support tool that EPA is distributing nationally to selected communities. Smart Growth INDEX was developed for EPA by Criterion Planners/ Engineers (an ESRI Business Partner) of Portland, Oregon, as a customization of Criterion's INDEX software series. The firm builds custom INDEX applications using ESRI's MapObjects and ArcView.

With help from the EPA's Dallas regional office and the Washington, D.C., headquarters staff, the San Antonio shareholders used INDEX to examine ideas and synthesize their visions and goals into a single, consensus-based plan. INDEX rates planning scenarios with a set of indicators that measure a scenario's performance in land use, transportation, urban design, and environmental terms. Example indicators include residential and employment density, walking distances to neighborhood amenities, and air pollutant emissions.

According to VIA's Project Manager Lance Freeman, "This type of GIS application is a great example of how the technology can bring diverse interests together and help build consensus. Previously, we had multiple viewpoints competing for people's attention. INDEX knits these together so that people can see the sum of the parts." Working collaboratively, stakeholders completed the following activities under the direction of the local chapter of the American Institute of Architects:

- The kickoff was a neighborhood planning workshop to solicit concerns and ideas from 75 residents and businesses in the area. This session produced valuable outlines of several potential futures that were later distilled into a preferred concept plan.

Case Study: Developing San Antonio's "Broadway Corridor" (cont.)

- A single database for the area was assembled from shareholder organizations. This process was significantly enhanced by the use of ArcGIS 8.1. Freeman observed, "With data coming in from so many sources, we couldn't have met our deadlines without version 8.1's direct reading of multiple data formats and advanced editing tools. We saved several days of work with the power of version 8.1."

- INDEX modeling was performed on three cases: (1) existing conditions to be used as benchmarks for evaluating alternative plans, (2) build-out of several current official plans for the areas that promote traditional auto-oriented uses, and (3) build-out of the workshop's preferred plan that promotes a mix of uses served by a multimodal transportation system. The objective was to determine which plan was most responsive to shareholder goals. See Figure 1.

- Shareholders reconvened to examine INDEX results, make refinements to their strategy, and prepare for the next implementation steps. A key component of the modeling was the use of ArcView Network Analyst. This ArcView extension is used in INDEX to simulate multimodal travel conditions in a study area that includes walking, biking, and transit. For each urban design scenario, ArcView Network Analyst is used to quickly gauge travel mode availabilities, distances, and route directness. As a result, every household and business in the area can be accurately characterized in terms of accessibility to essential services and amenities. According to Eliot Allen of Criterion Planners/Engineers, "With ESRI's help, we've been able to develop ArcView Network Analyst into an essential diagnostic tool that truly integrates land use and transportation planning at the neighborhood level."

Figure 1. San Antonio's Broadway Corridor

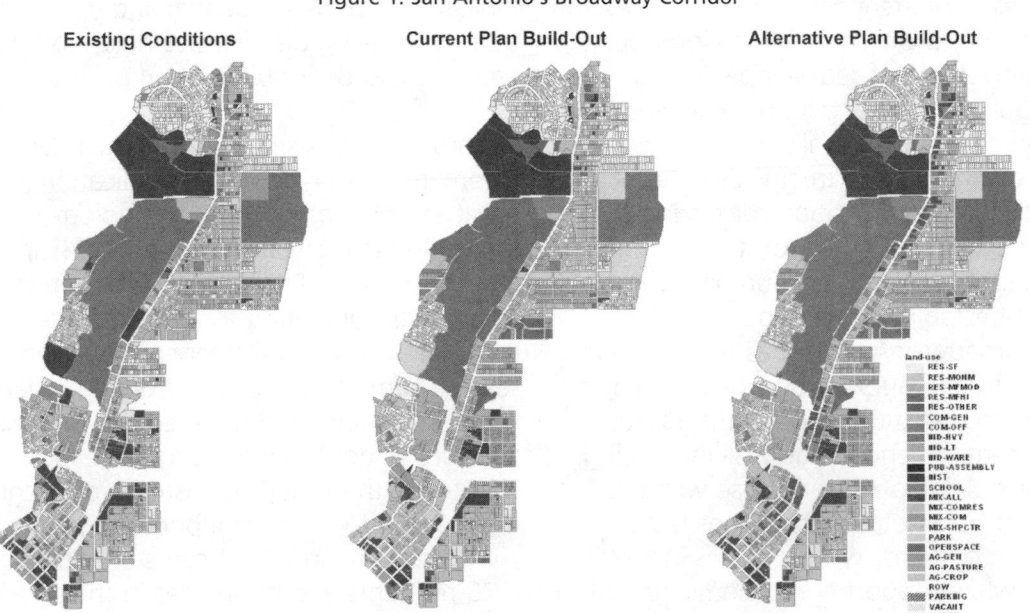

Existing Conditions   Current Plan Build-Out   Alternative Plan Build-Out

San Antonio's Broadway Corridor was modeled three ways in INDEX: existing conditions, current plan build-out, and stakeholders' alternative plan build-out. The latter emphasizes mixed live/work/shop land-uses where the current plan focuses on auto-oriented strip commercial.

Case Study: Developing San Antonio's "Broadway Corridor" (cont.)

The final INDEX "report card" for the Corridor produced several important findings. First, it confirmed the area as worthy of attention for redevelopment. Of the 40 INDEX indicators, one-quarter of them already scored favorably under existing conditions, and only five were rated unfavorable. Second, it showed that the current official plan for the area would lead to some, but not major, improvements over existing conditions. The number of indicators scoring in the favorable range increased by only one, and the number in the unfavorable range decreased by only one. Most important, it revealed that the shareholders' new proposed plan would create much better conditions than the current plan. The number of favorably scored indicators jumped to 17, and the

unfavorable count dropped to only three. In this way, the GIS tool gave participants rapid, critical feedback on the validity of their work to date and the promise of their future efforts.

Following the review of initial INDEX results, organizations have continued to improve the area's database and to model additional variations of the basic concepts. Emphasis is being given to public information and agency coordination in anticipation of program and capital improvement commitments during 2002.

Source:
Freeman and Allen 2005 (E). Reprinted with permission from the authors.

Notes

_____

_____

_____

_____

_____

_____

_____

_____

_____

_____

_____

_____

_____

_____

_____

_____

Neighborhood Design

4

Students explore the current design of their neighborhood, critically evaluate a variety of development options, and formulate ideas for guiding further change or growth in their neighborhood.

Subjects
Environmental Studies, Graphic Arts, Social Studies

Note: If time permits, we suggest that you first conduct the activity titled "Mapping Your Community through Time," whereby students investigate the building blocks of their community such as housing, transportation, green infrastructure, and industry.

Concepts
2.10 Cultural and societal perspectives influence the attitudes, beliefs, and biases of people toward the use of resources and environmental protection.

3.10 In democratic societies, individuals and groups, working through governmental channels, can influence the way public and private lands and resources are managed.

4.6 Human-built environments, if planned, constructed, and landscaped to be compatible with the environment in which they will be located, can conserve resources, enhance environmental quality, and promote the comfort and well-being of those who will live within them.

Skills
Analyzing, Evaluating, Identifying Attributes and Components, Inferring, Observing, Predicting, Summarizing

Materials
Copies of student pages

Time Considerations
Part A: One 50-minute period

Part B: Three 50-minute periods

Objectives
▶ Students will conduct a field survey to investigate change or growth patterns in their neighborhood.

▶ Students will explore the role of planners in shaping their communities' current and future forms.

▶ Students will analyze the layout of their community.

Assessments
▶ Have students imagine that they are the founders of their community. Tell them to write a letter describing the challenges and triumphs of creating the new neighborhood.

▶ Have students evaluate their neighborhood from the perspective of different "user groups," such as commuters, elementary school children, business owners, families, and senior citizens. Students might also conduct interviews to learn more.

▶ Assign students the task of creating a brochure for prospective neighborhood residents.

▶ Ask students to write a mini–case study for their neighborhood, following the models provided on the student pages titled "Different Development Options."

▶ Invite students to write GreenWorks! grants that would benefit their community.

Background

Lively, diverse, intense cities contain the seeds of their own regeneration, with energy enough to carry over for problems and needs outside themselves.

—Jane Jacobs (B)

What Is Planning?

Who decides how the pieces of a community should and will fit together? According to the American Planning Association, the goal of city and regional planning is to further the welfare of people and their communities by creating convenient, equitable, healthful, efficient, and aesthetically pleasing environments for present and future generations. **Planners** are people who collaborate with interest groups, citizens, and public officials to develop a vision of the future and to build on that vision.[1]

Planners work with many types of communities—small villages, rural areas, large cities, suburban towns, and even counties and states. Though communities are often bound by existing zoning laws and other regulations, planners help community leaders and citizens look at existing trends, conditions, and options for development and change. Planners develop and analyze plans for **land use** patterns, including housing needs; parks and recreation opportunities; highways, streets, sidewalks, bike lanes, and other transportation systems; and economic development. By its nature, planning is interdisciplinary because planners consider the social conditions, demographics, safety issues, visual character, air and water quality, and requests and needs of the community. Plans are presented to community officials, who—with input from many interested parties—review, revise, and adopt them for action. Once the plans have been adopted, the planner's job shifts to coordinating work among many groups and implementing the plan.[2]

Design and Planning

What's the difference between planning and design? The two terms are often used interchangeably, but many people in the field do distinguish between them. Urban design is the generally accepted name for the process of giving physical design direction to urban growth, conservation, and change. It is understood to include the landscape, as well as the buildings—both preservation and new construction—and both rural areas and cities.[3] Design can differ from planning in scale. The scale of design might be that of a street, park, or transit stop, as opposed to a larger region or community. Design lies somewhere between art, whose object is beauty, and planning, whose object is functionality.[4]

Traditional Neighborhood or Sprawl?

How do the physical building blocks of your community fit together? Up until World War II, the **traditional neighborhood** in North America was fundamentally the same as a European settlement. While not perfect, the traditional model—represented by mixed-use and pedestrian-friendly communities with a grid street system, higher density, and effective transit—has proven to be a sustainable and reliable form of growth. In some parts of the world, the traditional neighborhood is still a dominant pattern of settlement, as it has been throughout recorded history.

Signs that you're in a traditional neighborhood include pedestrians who are walking and shopping on aesthetically pleasing streets, and offices and homes that are integrated into commercial areas—for example, apartments and offices located above stores. Other signs of a traditional neighborhood are a variety of housing types, attractive public **green spaces**, subtle signage, homes with front porches (or other street-level gathering spaces), and local places where people gather.

Contrasting with traditional neighborhoods are areas characterized by spread-out development—otherwise known as **sprawl**. Sprawling growth manifests itself in low-density suburban development, large expanses of single-use zones (such as separate commercial, residential, and industrial zones), heavy dependence on automobiles, traffic, office parks, **big-box stores** and chain franchises, large parking lots, a scarcity of pedestrian access, disappearing green space and farmland, a shortage of **open spaces**, and **visual pollution**.

Growth is inevitable, but it does not have to be sprawling or uncontrolled. It can be well-planned, visually appealing, affordable, and channeled into appropriate locations. Across the country, many urban, suburban, and rural neighborhoods are choosing to manage growth so that it supports environmental protection, improved quality of life, equitable housing, and a sense of place.

Zoning

One of the enablers of sprawl is conventional *zoning*. The reasons for zoning can be traced back to the previous century when the Industrial Revolution wrought terrible environmental and social chaos on the cities. "City dwellers were deafened and choked by the roaring fumes of rail and industry both day and night."[5] City planners wisely advocated the separation of factories from homes, with remarkable results. Life expectancies rose significantly, and the planners were hailed as heroes. The original idea was to separate incompatible uses, but in recent times, it has been applied so that all uses become separate.[6] Not all conventional zoning regulations will lead to inefficient land use. For instance, zoning can lead to the preservation of certain places, such as coastal areas. Nonetheless, many people are rethinking conventional zoning because certain elements can stifle innovation and sustainable growth. In place of conventional zoning, many people are advocating *mixed-use neighborhoods* that incorporate design guidelines to provide for visually, environmentally, economically, and socially responsible growth.

Stopping Sprawl

Conventional zoning is only one of the practices under close scrutiny by advocates of better-planned development. *Smart growth* is a term coined to describe development that serves the economy, the community, and the environment by providing a framework for communities to make informed decisions about how and where they grow.[7] Unfortunately, smart growth in some communities has negative connotations associated with it. Smart growth proponents are quick to point out that they are not antigrowth and that the many problems associated with sprawl are not caused by growth per se; those problems are caused by inefficient, unplanned growth.[8]

Here is a list of 10 smart growth principles.[9] There are many more, but these 10 are meant to be examples. Further information and examples are found in the student pages titled "Different Development Options."

1. Mix land uses.

2. Take advantage of compact building design.

3. Create a range of housing opportunities.

4. Create walkable, bikeable neighborhoods.

5. Foster distinctive, attractive communities with a strong sense of place.

6. Preserve openspace, farmland, natural beauty, and critical environmental areas.

7. Strengthen and direct development toward existing communities.

8. Provide a variety of transportation choices.

9. Make development decisions predictable, fair, and cost-effective.

10. Encourage community and stakeholder collaboration in development decisions.

The average American driver spends 443 hours per year—the equivalent of 55 eight-hour workdays—behind the wheel. Residents of sprawling communities drive three to four times as much as those living in compact, well-planned areas.[10] One way to increase transportation choices is through *transit-oriented development*, which promotes high-density yet diverse individual housing, retail franchises, employment opportunities, and other services in a concentrated area and in the proximity (about one-quarter mile) of transit stations. To accomplish transit-oriented development, communities need to ensure that their zoning **ordinances** allow for increased density and mixed-use near transit stops. Increasing community density generally results in spending less for roads, parking lots and garages, water and sewer systems, and other forms of neighborhood infrastructure.

Polls show that Americans strongly support finding more ways to manage growth. In fact, according to the Millennium Planning Survey conducted by the American Planning Association in 2000, 78 percent of voters believe that it is important for the U.S. Congress to help communities solve problems associated with growth.[11] Many development options for managed growth can be implemented on pieces of land known as **brownfields**. Brownfields are parcels of land that are lying vacant because the presence of a contaminant hinders their redevelopment. In 1995, the Environmental Protection Agency (EPA) created a new program that focused on providing financial assistance to communities wanting to redevelop brownfields. As a result, this program reduces development pressures on open space, creates new jobs, and allows for the use of existing infrastructure. The EPA has estimated that more than 500,000 brownfields exist throughout the United States in rural communities, suburbs, and urban areas.[12] Since the program was initiated, more than 922 brownfield sites in 153 cities have been redeveloped.[13]

Pro-sprawl and Anti-smart Growth?

If sprawl is so bad, why is it so common? Not everyone supports the smart growth movement or agrees that sprawl is negative. It is important to remember that today's sprawl is yesterday's idealistic solution. The automobile gave us the means to spread out in search of the good life, a tradition dating back to the Pilgrims and Daniel Boone.[14] And for some, spread-out development may still be today's idealistic

solution. For example, author and professor of economics Randall Holcombe argues, "Nobody forces people to live in single-family detached homes. Developers build them because that is where people want to live." Holcombe and others criticize the smart growth movement for suggesting that government regulation, as opposed to market forces, should dictate land use decisions.[15] According to a report released by the Cato Institute, a nonprofit, public policy research foundation, smart growth plans contribute to workplace inaccessibility by increasing housing costs, thus making it difficult for some people to locate near areas that are growing economically.[16]

Other critics of smart growth claim that people may not support smart growth once they realize some of the affects of changing policies. According to David Riggs, people are starting to realize that **compact development** means more crowding, rising traffic congestion, and longer commutes—outcomes that are antithetical to their choosing the convenience and spaciousness of the suburbs.[17] Other critics claim that sprawl

is blamed for more than its fair share of societal ills. Some people disagree with the argument that urban sprawl gives rise to excessively costly infrastructure, high transportation costs, and environmental damage.[18]

Endnotes

1 American Planning Association 2003 (E).
2 American Planning Association 2003 (E).
3 Barnett 1982 (A).
4 Ewing 1999 (C).
5 Gillham 2002 (A).
6 Duany, Plater-Zyberk, and Speck 2000 (A).
7 Smart Growth Network/ICMA 2002 (C).
8 Bollier 1998 (A).
9 Smart Growth Network/ICMA 2002 (C).
10 Sierra Club 2002 (E).
11 Benfield Terris, and Vorsanger 2001 (A).
12 EPA 2004a (E).
13 ENR Staff 2003 (B).
14 Dietrich 1999 (B).
15 Holcombe 1999 (C); Stroup 2002 (A).
16 Cato Institute 2000 (E).
17 Riggs 1999 (C).
18 Gordon 2000 (B).

Letters following author and date citations refer to sections in the bibliography (Appendix B) where the reader can find full data about the sources cited.

Getting Ready

- Write the following questions on the board:
  - Where are the residences located?
  - Where are the businesses located?
  - Where are the public spaces (e.g., schools, parks, library) located?
  - Is your neighborhood aesthetically pleasing?
  - Are there areas of your neighborhood that suffer from various kinds of environmental, noise, or visual pollution?
  - What kinds of public transportation are available? Is your neighborhood pedestrian and bike friendly? Why or why not?
  - Are there areas in your neighborhood that feel unsafe to visit?
- Review and photocopy the student pages "Different Development Options" and "Neighborhood Design Questionnaire."
- Contact a planner or designer if you plan to invite one to speak to your students.

Doing the Activity

Part A

1. Give students a few minutes to describe— through words or a sketch—the layout of their neighborhood. Ask students to consider the questions on the board as they create their descriptions or drawings.

2. Invite a few students to share their descriptions or drawings, and briefly discuss the questions on the board.

3. Then ask students these questions: Who decided the layout of the neighborhood? Who decided what types of transportation would be available? Who decided what the neighborhood would look like? Draw on the information from the earlier "Background" section, and discuss the role of planners, designers, politicians, and citizen groups.

4. Encourage students to explore the thinking that may have shaped some of their community's features. For example, why might planners or politicians have built an industrial complex? Why would a large mall be at the outskirts of town? What is the current transportation system, and why was it established that way? What are the benefits of this layout? Help students realize that even if their community exhibits characteristics of sprawl or has features that appear poorly planned according to today's standards, those features may be a result of well-intentioned growth efforts or they may reflect market forces at the time.

Part B

5. Provide students with the student pages titled "Different Development Options," which feature mini–case studies describing different community designs. Mention that the different designs are not necessarily mutually exclusive and that a single neighborhood can exhibit elements of multiple designs. Give students time to read the case studies. *Optional*: Divide the class into groups: one for each design choice. Instruct the

groups to read about their community design and to create a poster. Have groups present their posters to the rest of the class.

6. Explain that as a next step, students will investigate their neighborhood to see if it contains some of the elements described in the case studies. For example, they could ask the following: Does your community have mixed-use development? What ways can people travel around your community? Compare neighborhood sketches from part A with examples of smart growth alternatives shown in the student pages titled "Different Development Options."

7. Distribute the student page titled "Neighborhood Design Questionnaire." For homework, have students walk through their neighborhood to complete the questions as best they can. You might encourage students to work in small groups. Students can also use their walk to make any changes or additions to the neighborhood drawing or description from step 1. *Optional*: Have students brainstorm to create their own questionnaire in class. Distribute this list to students, and have them complete it during their walk. *Optional*: If your students live in a rural area, have them bring in a community map. Ask students to complete the questionnaire according to what they see on the map.

8. When students are back in class, break them into small groups of two or three students. Have them refer to the case studies and their completed "Neighborhood Design Questionnaires." Then have them analyze their respective neighborhoods on the basis of whether they think those neighborhoods incorporate the development options highlighted in each case study.

9. Initiate a class discussion; then draw on the following questions:
• What are the positive and negative attributes of each development option?

• How is your neighborhood similar to, or different from, the neighborhoods described in the case studies?
• What are the positive and negative attributes of your neighborhood?
• Do you think all development options would be appropriate for your neighborhood? Why or why not?
• How has your community's design contributed to your sense of place?

Part C

10. Have students work in small groups to create a list of attributes that they think would make a great neighborhood. Students should draw on, but not be limited to, ideas discussed in class. Perhaps assign this exercise in conjunction with Activity 6 "A Vision for the Future".

11. Have students present their plans to the rest of the class.

12. In a concluding discussion, compare and contrast students' ideas.

13. Next, present the following questions for each student to answer: What would you most like to change about your neighborhood design, and what would you most like to stay the same? (In answering, students should refer to their attribute lists.) Ask students to come up with a plan for change and a plan for protecting what they want to remain the same. Plans should address whom they would need to contact to implement the plan.

14. *Optional*: Encourage students to compare their lists to the list of the 10 smart growth principles presented in the "Background" and by the Smart Growth Network at www.smartgrowth.org. The goal is not for students to evaluate whether their own ideas are right or wrong, but for them to examine their lists in the light of ideas professionals are debating today.

- As a real-world extension, share your class's findings and suggestions with local planners, officials, or the public. Consider a newspaper article, letter, meeting, or presentation.

- Have students play the role of lawmaker. What new ordinances or laws would be needed for their plans to succeed? Are there other ways to achieve success (e.g., incentives, public education)?

- Are there any elements of the students' designs that can be implemented? Have students research what it would take to implement a new community design element, create a plan, and see it through (see GreenWorks! at www.plt.org).

- Invite a planner or designer to speak to your students about what that person does. Have students prepare questions ahead of time. Perhaps even have the planner or designer evaluate the students' plans.

- Take a field trip to a nearby community that is implementing a new design or to one that is different from the community where the students live. Have them evaluate the new community and then compare and contrast it with their own.

- Use the "Safe Routes to Schools" toolkit (visit www.saferoutestoschools.org), which has instructions for analyzing your school site to see how safe and easy it is to walk and bike to school, as well as tips for working with school administrators, town and county planners, politicians, and local neighbors to make changes. It also instructs students about how to start programs that promote walking, biking, carpooling, and taking public transportation.

Different Development Options—Transit-Oriented Development

Transit-oriented development (TOD) focuses on improving and efficiently using existing mass transit systems in community planning and design. By building around light-rail stations, improving bus stations, and encouraging ridership, TODs hope to reduce car use and offer a cheap and convenient alternative to driving. The Metro subway system in Washington, D.C., is a notable success story of transit-oriented development.

Planners have worked to encourage development both adjacent to and above the Metro stations. The Washington Metropolitan Area Transit Authority (WMATA) has supported 40 development projects over the past 20 years to create vibrant business and residential communities around the subway stations and to encourage people to use the train. In Arlington County, Virginia, nearly 30 million square feet of commercial development, 25,000 units of housing, and 10,000 hotel rooms have been built in clustered "neighborhoods" around Metro stations since the 1970s.

Since opening in 1976, the subway network has grown to five lines, consisting of 86 stations and 106 miles (170.5 km) of track. There were 190 million trips on Metrorail in 2004, meaning about 520,000 passengers use the system every day. The system is the second busiest in the nation, behind only the New York City Subway. Metro stations such as the one at Dupont Circle are great models of pedestrian-friendly development. Dupont Circle is surrounded by a diversity of shops, restaurants, offices, housing, and parks conveniently connected by a grid of sidewalks, streets, and diagonal boulevards. (See Figure 1.)

The WMATA and other groups are still hard at work looking for new ways to promote Metro use. Current projects include extending hours of operation and trying to make some Metro stations safer, more accessible to pedestrians and bikers, and better connected to bus access. A mixture of residential, office, and commercial development is actively encouraged around the stations.

Figure 1

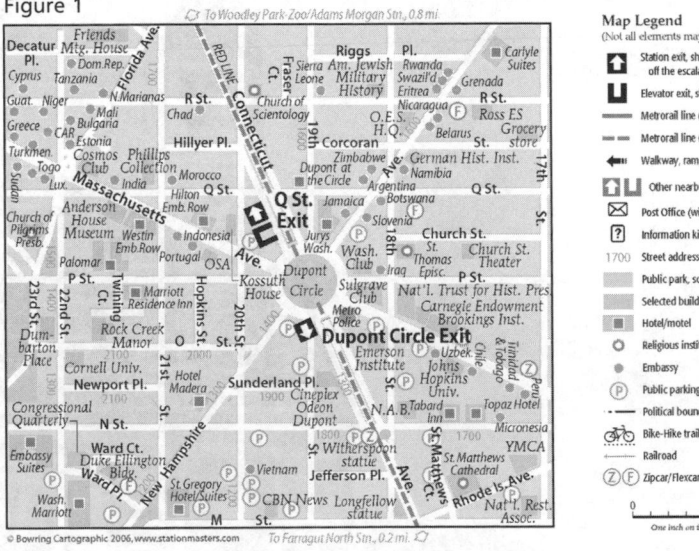

Sources: Delaware Valley Regional Planning Commission 2001 (E); Washington Regional Network for Livable Communities 2005 (E); Washington Metro Transit Authority 2005 (E); and "Making the Case for Transit" at www.wmata.com

Different Development Options—Pedestrian and Bicycle-Oriented Development

Development in suburbs or other areas of outlying sprawl is typically unfriendly to bikes or pedestrians. In many cases, we have separated the places where we live from the places where we shop, work, and play, thus causing us to drive from place to place. Many U.S. streets are not safe to walk or ride on because they are designed to move motor vehicles in large volumes and at high speeds. At other times, people are forced to walk in the street because many areas lack sidewalks. Other areas may also feature dead-end cul-de-sacs, which can limit accessibility.

Copyright Project for Public Spaces, Inc. www.pps.org

Adding crosswalks, sidewalks, bicycle paths, bike parking, and special bike lanes on streets increases the chance that people will choose to walk or bike to reach their destinations. The multiple benefits of walking and biking are environmentally friendly and important to a healthy lifestyle. Key features that encourage walking are narrow streets, sidewalks at least five feet wide, rows of trees and on-street parking to buffer pedestrians from the road, a mix of land uses, safe crossings, comfortable and safe places to wait, and streets designed for slow traffic.

Portland, Oregon, has found a way to make the city safe for bicyclists. It has a policy that requires accommodation of bicycles in all new road construction, reconstruction, and resurfacing projects. Bike racks or storage units are provided at all libraries, transit stations, government buildings, and retail centers. To maintain safety, Portland uses warning and regulatory signs, traffic-calming devices, enforcement, and colored bike lanes. The city, several nonprofit organizations, and some employers have incentive programs to encourage bike riding, including gift certificates, cash-back programs, and lottery tickets. Portland's "Safe Routes to School" program helps participating schools become familiar with bicycle facilities in their school's service area. The program also helps schools identify routes used by students and parents to get to school, and it removes barriers to biking. Portland's bicycle programs have experienced great success. There has been a consistent growth in the number of bicycle trips (in 1992, there were 3,555 daily bicycle trips across the bridges; in 2002, the number grew to 8,250—a growth of 130 percent over those 10 years). According to U.S. Census data, 2,556 people identified the bicycle as their

Copyright Project for Public Spaces, Inc. www.pps.org

Different Development Options— Pedestrian and Bicycle-Oriented Development (cont.)

primary means of transportation to work in 1990; 5,013 people identified the bicycle as their primary means in 2000.

Some countries in Europe have chosen quite different methods to provide safe streets for bicyclists and pedestrians. For example, Holland has special shared streets called *woonerfs*, which literally means "streets for living." Instead of having separate sidewalks and bike paths, slow car traffic on a woonerf mixes with other activities, such as people walking, cycling, or playing in the street. The street turns into a social space, where people can sit, chat, sip coffee, or watch the world go by.

Drivers on woonerfs slow down to roughly walking speeds because they realize other people are using the street. Bikers and pedestrians feel comfortable because they are not dodging high-speed traffic. Some streets have trees, planters, parking areas, and other obstacles right in the street—causing drivers to slow down and pay attention to what's happening around them.

Statistically, shared streets are safer than the kinds of streets we are used to in the United States. Shared streets also encourage biking and walking, thereby helping to reduce pollution and to provide a better quality of life. Today, Holland has more than 7,000 woonerfs. The idea emerged from Holland in the 1970s, and shared streets are now well established in mainland Europe. In the United States, Boulder, Colorado, and Davis, California, are experimenting with the idea.

Sources:
Campbell 2005 (E)
Ewing 1999 (C)
Hamilton-Baillie 2001 (E)
Home Zone News 2005 (E)
Local Government Commission Center for Livable Communities 2003 (E).

Different Development Options—Mixed-Use Development

Cities have tradition-
ally integrated shopping,
housing, and businesses
into one area, but since
the end of World War
II, suburban zoning has
segregated those areas.
The subsequent migra-
tion of residents, stores,
and jobs to the suburbs
greatly affected both the
commercial and residen-
tial areas of many cities.
The older pattern of
closely connected neigh-
borhoods that featured
small shops, local restaurants, and affordable
housing was replaced by
suburban sprawl with its

Copyright Project for Public Spaces, Inc. www.pps.org

massive residential neighborhoods and choked
commercial thoroughfares. One solution to
this problem is implementing a mixed-use
development strategy. Mixed-use development
is often defined as locating land uses with
complementary functions close together, such
as apartments or houses, shops, offices, places
of worship, recreational facilities, and other
structures that meet the needs of residents.
Mixed-use development can be used effectively
in downtowns, neighborhood centers, transit
nodes, main streets, and some community
commercial centers.

The Union Square area, which is centered on
Union Square Park in New York City, provides
a classic example of mixed-use development
where pedestrians can walk to shops, offices,
recreational areas, and homes. Different uses
are concentrated in a small area as opposed to
being spread out, thus providing rich diversity
and complexity within a neighborhood where
cars are not needed.

Although vibrant today, Union Square Park
was undesirable and overrun by petty criminals
about 30 years ago. But in 1976, the situation
started to turn around when a farmers' market
opened, drawing produce from small regional
farms. The Greenmarket sparked a neighborhood revival and encouraged a diversity of
people to mingle in traditional urban ways. The
market also attracted restaurants to the area
because they could take advantage of easy
access to fresh produce. The city decided to
redesign the park, making it more pedestrian
friendly. As part of the rebirth, new businesses
opened around the park. Today, Union Square
is a vital neighborhood used by thousands of
people every day for different purposes. The
area's remarkable energy and dynamism can be
attributed in large part to its diversity.

Sources:
Gratz 2002 (E).
Oregon Transportation and Growth
Management 2001 (C).
Project for Public Spaces Inc. 2003 (E).

Different Development Options—Compact Development

Sprawl is often characterized as the haphazard, low-density, inefficient use of land and resources occurring outside urban areas. Compact development is an alternative to sprawl because it limits urban movement into rural areas by revitalizing and efficiently using the existing land within urban areas. Compact development requires a consciousness of how to use land to its maximum efficiency, as well as innovative planning and design to reuse or renovate inefficient or abandoned land. In some cases, land may be contaminated by the presence of hazardous substances or other types of pollutants. This land is known as a "brownfield" and requires all contaminates to be removed before development can occur.

Atlanta, Georgia, has been experiencing population growth; between 1992 and 2002, more than 700,000 people moved to the area. This growth has had negative consequences for air quality and road congestion. Atlanta is classified as a marginal nonattainment area according to the Environmental Protection Agency's regulations for the 8-hour National Ambient Air Quality Standard for ground-level ozone. The 2004 Urban Mobility Study by the Texas Transportation Institute revealed that Atlanta now ranks sixth in the nation on its travel-time index (a ratio comparing time spent traveling during rush hour to time spent traveling the same route during free-flow periods). (See Figure 1.) In 1992, Atlanta was ranked as the 33rd most congested city; in 2002, it was ranked 6th.

However, a development project called Atlantic Station is bringing hope and progress to this area of the city. Close to midtown Atlanta, Atlantic Station will transform an abandoned brownfield site (where heavy metals were once milled) into a transit-accessible and pedestrian-friendly complex of homes, offices, and shops. In fact, the project represents the largest cleanup of an industrial site in the southeastern United States to date.

The plans call for a 138-acre, 12-million-square-foot development, which includes parks, lakes, and other urban refuges. Atlantic Station will also contain 3,200 residential units, a technology center with 4 to 5 million square feet of office space, three hotels, and 1.5 million square feet of shopping and entertainment space.

Figure 1 Travel-Time Index Ranking, 1992–2002

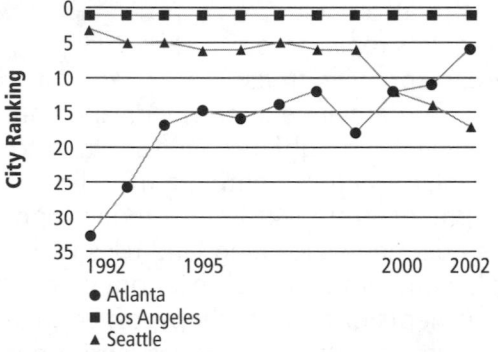

- Atlanta
- Los Angeles
- Seattle

Atlantic Station has easy access to the subway and other transit options. A new bridge was built to connect the area with midtown Atlanta. Atlantic Station will help reduce the amount of driving required by redeveloping an old site near the city center (as opposed to using open space at the outskirts) and by providing a compact "city inside a city" design that provides homes, shopping, and offices in walkable distance. Among the benefits of less driving are less time spent in traffic, increased physical activity, decreased emission of greenhouse gasses, and a reduced contribution to Atlanta's smog problem.

Different Development Options—Compact Development (cont.)

Redevelopment of the site has had its share of difficulties. Developer Stephen Macauley has said, "Everything in the process of development … is formatted to support conventional development. Layered on that, at every level of governmental approval is a staff … unaccustomed to mixed-use developments." Still, Atlantic Station is progressing and as of early 2006 it provides homes for nearly 10,000 people and employment opportunities for approximately 30,000 people.

Sources:
Atlantic Station, LLP 2005 (E).
Benfield, Terris, and Vorsanger 2001 (A).
Environmental Protection Agency Green Book 2004 (E).
Pendered 2004 (B).
Texas Transportation Institute 2004 (E).

Different Development Options—Conservation-Oriented Development

Conservation-oriented development strives to promote land development while simultaneously preserving open space, farmland, scenic view-sheds, natural beauty, wildlife habitat, and other critical environmental areas. It brings together two sides that are often at odds: conservationists and land developers. Conservation-oriented development clusters concentrates housing and development in specific areas, while preserving other areas in their natural, undeveloped state—both for ecological purposes and as an amenity for residents. Concentrating development can also help communities save money by reducing the costs of infrastructure such as sewers, roads, and utilities.

One community that is implementing conservation-oriented development practices is Chester County in southeastern Pennsylvania. Chester County is characterized by rolling farmland, stream-filled valleys and woodlands, horse farms, and valuable historic landmarks. Yet Chester County is also Pennsylvania's fastest-growing county, largely because of the expanding nearby cities of Philadelphia, Pennsylvania, and Wilmington, Delaware. In fact, in 1995, county planners estimated that all of the county's farmland would be gone within 40 years at the current rate of development. In response to development threats, Chester County decided to take action to combat sprawl and preserve its natural treasures.

The Chester County Planning Commission started revising its comprehensive plan, including both citizens and local officials in the process. The planning commission used an insert in a local newspaper to gather information about the public's views. Respondents overwhelmingly preferred denser, less-sprawling development in targeted areas, as opposed to the current haphazard patterns of growth. The commission identified areas and characteristics to preserve, as well as the areas most suited for new development. Conferences and workshops encouraged community participation in the process.

The result of those planning efforts was a guide to growth through 2020. The plan distinguished four distinct types of landscape in the county: natural, rural, suburban, and urban. The plan also incorporates growth boundaries that concentrate all future development within agreed-upon areas while preserving other areas. The success of Chester County's plans to combat sprawl and to preserve open space remains to be seen. However, so far the county's efforts have earned an Outstanding Planning Award from the American Planning Association and have provided a hopeful model for other communities.

Sources:
Benfield, Terris, and Vorsanger 2001 (A).
Environmental Protection Agency 2001 (C).

Different Development Options—Suburban Development

People have long escaped the city to buy a piece of property with a single-family home in the suburbs. This trend occurred throughout the 1900s, increasing particularly as the automobile gained popularity and made it more feasible for people to live farther away from city centers. The suburb of Radburn, outside Fairlawn, New Jersey, is considered one of the first automobile-inspired suburbs.

Established in 1927, Radburn was designed to accommodate both automobiles and pedestrians. Roads were built specifically for automobiles and were sized according to the estimated amount of traffic. Wide streets outside the community carried the heaviest traffic, and narrower roads with cul-de-sacs ran through residential neighborhoods. The cul-de-sacs limited the amount of traffic that could pass through a clustered neighborhood, thus making the streets safer for pedestrians and children.

Overpasses, underpasses, and pathways (collectively called "greenways") were constructed to provide safe routes for pedestrian travel. Furthermore, the entrances to homes were turned away from the street and instead faced private gardens and the entrances to pedestrian greenways.

The variety of housing types, small neighborhood retail centers, and interior green spaces helped make Radburn an ideal community for young families. Later, many of those innovations would become standard features of subdivisions across the country.

Source:
Gillham 2002 (A).

Neighborhood Design Questionnaire

1. What is the name and location of your neighborhood?

2. When was your neighborhood established?

3. What are the primary modes of transportation?

4. What types of residences are there? (e.g., apartments, single-family homes, townhouses, mobile homes, farms)

5. What other types of buildings can you find? (e.g., office buildings, public buildings, shops, university buildings, restaurants)

6. Are there trees and green spaces in your neighborhood? If so, describe those areas.

7. What types of habitat are available for wildlife (e.g., open water, residential area, forest)?

8. Do you feel safe walking around your neighborhood? Why or why not?

9. What else do you observe about your neighborhood?

10. Please circle your responses.

To get to	I could			
School	walk	take public transportation	ride/drive in a car	bike
Shopping	walk	take public transportation	ride/drive in a car	bike
Restaurants	walk	take public transportation	ride/drive in a car	bike
Library	walk	take public transportation	ride/drive in a car	bike
Recreation	walk	take public transportation	ride/drive in a car	bike

To get to	I usually			
School	walk	take public transportation	ride/drive in a car	bike
Shopping	walk	take public transportation	ride/drive in a car	bike
Restaurants	walk	take public transportation	ride/drive in a car	bike
Library	walk	take public transportation	ride/drive in a car	bike
Recreation	walk	take public transportation	ride/drive in a car	bike

Green Space

5

Students investigate green infrastructure and native plant communities at the neighborhood, community, and regional scales and then explore the dual needs of accommodating population growth while protecting green space and native plant communities.

Subjects
Ecology, Environmental Science, Geology

Concepts
3.4 Ecosystems possess measurable indicators of environmental health.

3.10 In democratic societies, individuals and groups, working through governmental channels, can influence the way public and private lands and resources are managed.

4.6 Human-built environments, if planned, constructed, and landscaped to be compatible with the environment in which they will be located, can conserve resources, enhance environmental quality, and promote the comfort and well-being of those who will live within them.

5.4 Ecosystems change over time through patterns of growth and succession. They are also affected by other phenomena such as disease, insects, fire, weather, climate, and human intervention.

Skills
Analyzing, Classifying and Categorizing, Comprehending, Identifying Attributes and Components, Interpreting, Observing, Predicting, Problem Solving

Materials
Copies of student pages, aerial photographs

Time Constraints
Part A: One 50-minute period

Part B: Two 50-minute periods

Part C: One or two 50-minute periods

Objectives
▶ Students will examine and discuss the social, health, ecological, and economic benefits of green space.

▶ Students will conduct a field inventory to collect data on their community's green infrastructure.

▶ Students will compare and contrast case studies illustrating a citywide and a statewide initiative to protect green space.

▶ Students will use maps to evaluate their community's green infrastructure and will design ideas for improving the network.

▶ Students will study local population growth trends and will explore the balance between protecting and developing community green space.

Assessments
▶ Encourage students to draw on the model of "Tall Tree Tales" as they develop their own list of the benefits of trees and open space locally. Each point on the list should be specific to your community (e.g., protecting the 20-acre swamp near Oak Ridge shopping plaza would provide habitat for the endangered salamander and would help filter drinking water flowing to the Lake Blue reservoir). As a challenge, encourage students to also include drawbacks or costs of preserving local green space.

▶ Have students imagine that the mayor contracted with them to inventory the local green infrastructure and to write a report summarizing their findings and recommendations. Consider consolidating or integrating the individual reports into one report and then sending or presenting it to your local government.

▶ Have students develop their own action plans for contributing to the protection of green space. Establish criteria for evaluating the plans using the content of the activity.

▶ Assign students the task of investigating laws that affect green space development and conservation.

Background

A city without trees is like a world without poetry and music. Tree-lined streets are more than shaded passage-ways linking buildings. They give us a chance to bring nature into the heart of our communities, while linking us to our past.

—Henry Arnold, (B)

Where in your community can you relax under green trees and read a great book? Enjoy a summer picnic with family or friends? Teach a child to ride a bike? Listen for the sounds of birds in spring or decode the tracks of local wildlife in winter? Does your community still have green space or other natural areas for people to enjoy plus wildlife to inhabit?

Green Space and Open Space

What do the terms **green space** and **open space** mean? Often those terms are used interchangeably to refer to land that is not covered with concrete or asphalt. Yet not all open space is visibly green or completely undeveloped—a city plaza, a corner playground, a baseball field, or rolling farmland might all be referred to as open space. Furthermore, not all places that we label "green space" are verdant wildlands and nature preserves. For instance, city parks, wetlands, open desert areas, cemeteries, golf courses, bike paths, vacant lots, and streamside corridors might all be called green space. Some stretches of green space are designed primarily for human activities, others are protected for **biodiversity** and wildlife conservation, and still others might accommodate the needs of both. In this activity, the two terms are used interchangeably.

The Urban Forest

Remarkably, metropolitan areas collectively support nearly one-fourth of the nation's total tree canopy cover—some 74.4 billion trees. The term **urban forest** refers to the sum of street trees, residential trees, park trees, and greenbelt vegetation found in a city and its outskirts. An urban forest includes trees on unused public and private land, trees in transportation and utility corridors, and forests on **watershed** lands. In some areas of the United States, tree cover may be increasing (such as the Northeast, where trees are re-colonizing abandoned farmland). Yet in other parts of our country, especially in urban and suburban areas where approximately 80 percent of Americans live,[1] our trees are disappearing at disturbing—though sometimes unnoticed—rates to make way for development and for expanding population pressures.[2]

Urban foresters recommend that metropolitan areas strive for an overall tree cover of 40 percent (30 percent in the arid Southwest). However, according to a 2001 national study by American Forests, our nation's urban forests are missing 634,407,719 trees as the result of urban and suburban development.[3] In other words, we would need to plant 634 million trees nationwide to bring urban areas up to the 40 percent target.

Urban forests are a significant national resource. A 1999 study by American Forests found that the tree canopy in Washington, D.C. dropped from 37 percent to 21 percent between 1973 and 1997. As a result, stormwater runoff increased by 34 percent and 354,000 pounds of pollutants remained in the atmosphere (for more information, see "Values of Green Space" in this activity). Urban forests are of special value because they are where the overwhelming majority of the U.S. population lives, works, and plays. Furthermore, urban forests promise to increase in importance in the years ahead. As urbanization spreads into less-developed areas, a growing percentage of the nation's natural resources will become part of urban forest ecosystems. As development proceeds, increasing amounts of forest outside those systems will also be subject to urban influences. For example, surrounding forests may be subject to stress from increased human activities, the introduction of **invasive species**, fire, disease, and insects.[4]

To track changes in the composition of urban forests over time, urban foresters use **Geographic Information Systems** (GIS) and compare satellite images (see Activity 3 "Mapping Your Community Through Time" for more information on GIS). One study, analyzed the 3.9 million–acre Puget Sound watershed surrounding Seattle. Comparison of satellite photographs from 1962 and 1998 revealed that the amount of land with less than 20 percent tree-canopy coverage more than doubled during that time period, from 25 percent to 57 percent.[5] Similarly, the Baltimore and Washington, D.C. area and Atlanta each lost one-third or more of their heavy tree cover—or the areas that function most like natural forests—by protecting watersheds and providing wildlife habitat.[6] In fact, many cities have seen a decline in natural tree cover by as much as 30 percent over the past several decades.[7]

Other Green Spaces

Forests and trees are not the only kinds of green space under threat. The preservation of prime farmland and ranch land are also important examples of green space. According to the U.S. Department of Agriculture, from 1992 to 1997 more than 11 million acres of farmland and ranch land were converted to developed use, with agricultural land making up more than half that total. During that period, an average of more than one million agricultural acres were developed each year. And the rate is increasing—up 51 percent from the rate reported in the previous decade.[8] Much of the land under the greatest development pressure is prime farmland—termed "prime" because this farmland has the finest soils, requires the least amount of chemical or irrigation input, or is in greatest proximity to markets and transportation networks.[9]

Conversion of farmland will have economic implications. For instance, in Fresno, California, part of the state's fertile Central Valley and one of the nation's most productive farm counties, one million acres of farmland are expected to be converted to suburban and urban areas by the year 2040. Experts predict that this change could reduce the value of the valley's agricultural production by a cumulative $49 billion and could take a $76 billion bite out of various agricultural support businesses.[10]

Reappearing Green

As communities grapple with the challenges associated with growth, we see encouraging initiatives designed to reverse tree loss, to protect open space and **scenic viewsheds**, and to "green" local communities. Increasingly, communities are investing in parks, open space, farmland, forest protection, and other green space elements. Back in 1967, Boulder, Colorado, pioneered the use of a dedicated sales tax to fund

the preservation of open space. Today, Boulder has 41,000 acres of open space, largely in a ring of greenbelts that offer spectacular views of the Rocky Mountains.[11] Some communities have followed Boulder's lead, while other states and communities have found their own innovative ways to help fund green space conservation. In Minnesota, for example, 40 percent of the proceeds from the state lottery go to the state's Environment and Natural Resources Trust Fund. This initiative is expected to raise at least $700 million for land protection in Minnesota during the next 25 years.[12]

Portland, Oregon, initiated another progressive idea: the **urban growth boundary**. In 1980, Portland established a boundary strictly limiting development at the city's fringe. Critics warned that the boundary would stifle development and damage the region's economy. Instead, the number of jobs in the metropolitan area has increased by 57 percent.[13]

The Urban Resources Initiative, which is a partnership among a nonprofit organization, Yale University, and the Community Foundation of Greater New Haven, has created the Community Greenspace Program aimed at revitalizing and beautifying common areas across the city. The community forester, landscape architects, and other volunteers offer technical advice and supplies to residents as

Copyright Project for Public Spaces, Inc. www.pps.org

they work together to restore their community's greenspaces. In particular, residents focus their efforts on planting trees, flowers, and shrubs along streetscapes, abandoned lots, neglected front yards, public housing, and parks. Community Greenspace projects have the added benefit of establishing personal ties among participants.[14] None of those initiatives are perfect, and each effort has its critics. Yet, different models represent efforts to protect open space.

Value of Green Space

Too many community leaders feel they must choose between economic growth and open space protection. But no such choice is necessary. Open space protection is good for a community's health, stability, beauty, and quality of life. It is also good for the bottom line.

—Will Rogers in *The Economic Benefits of Parks* by S. Lerner and W. Poole (C)

Why should we care about green space? The aesthetic benefits are obvious but that may be difficult to quantify. Strolling along tree-lined streets, playing frisbee in a park, or catching a glimpse of local wildlife can help us stay connected with the natural world, even in a charged urban environment. Frederick Law Olmsted was a visionary 19th-century landscape architect who designed many renowned urban parks. He spoke of the need for parks and of a park's chief purpose as being "its effect on the human organism … like that of music … a kind that goes back of thought and cannot be fully given the form of words."[15]

Green space also offers social, economic, health, and ecological benefits that are often overlooked. Green space can bolster local economies, preserve critical environmental areas, provide recreational opportunities, and guide new growth into existing communities. Preservation of green space can have a profound effect on a community's quality of life—and,

therefore, a region's economic prosperity.[16] Social scientists have begun to document and understand the social value that vegetation can play in promoting a safe city environment. For example, research from the University of Illinois suggests that residents living in "greener" surroundings actually reported lower levels of fear, fewer incivilities, and less violent behavior.[17] Homebuyers are more attracted to neighborhoods that offer easy access to parks, playgrounds, trails, greenways, and natural open space. When a community decides which lands to protect, it helps define where development should occur, and it enables growth and protection of the natural environment at the same time. For example, clustered housing and **compact development** are cheaper for a community to service than housing on larger lots, primarily because such development consumes less land and requires less infrastructure, such as shorter roads and utility lines.[18]

Preserving green space is also essential for plant and wildlife populations and for the functioning of ecological processes and ecosystem services, such as providing pure water to drink and clean air to breathe. Wildlife populations and biodiversity decline without green space and the corridors that connect increasingly fragmented green spaces. Actively preserving green space offers the opportunity to promote a richer world for humans and wildlife. For additional examples of the many benefits of open space, please see the student page titled "Tall Tree Tales."

People need to understand that if you take that big block of green on the outskirts of town or in the heart of the neighborhood, you lose that restoration potential forever.

—Roger Ulrich

Can We Afford Green Space?

Does land conservation force a rise in local property taxes by removing land from the tax rolls? A study conducted by the Trust for Public Land in Massachusetts found a mixed answer. In the short term, property taxes did rise after a land conservation project. But in the long term, towns that had protected the most land enjoyed, on average, the lowest property tax rates. Perhaps this consequence is attributed to less development, which required less sewer and water infrastructure, roads, schools, and other services. Other economic benefits of open space conservation include boosting tourism revenues, increasing property values, attracting investment, stimulating commercial growth, revitalizing inner cities, safeguarding the future of farming economies, and preventing flood damage.[19]

Green Infrastructure

Green infrastructure offers a smart solution to our land conservation challenges because it seeks to plan land development and land conservation together in a way that is consistent with natural environmental patterns.

—**Mark Benedict and Edward T. McMahon (E)**

Where should green space be located in a community? Are all parks, trees, vegetation, and other green spaces equally valuable? What criteria determine the green health of a community? Increasingly, people are emphasizing the importance of not just planting a certain number of trees or vegetation per acre but creating a well-planned, interconnected network of green space. In conservation planning, emphasis on ecological process and interconnectedness has replaced the earlier focus on protection of particular species or on having direct human utility for specific geographic areas.[20]

The term **green infrastructure** can be described as follows (see Activity 3 "Mapping Your Community Through Time"):

"Green infrastructure is the nation's natural life support system—a strategically planned and managed network of wilderness, parks, greenways, conservation easements, and working lands with conservation value that supports native species, maintains natural ecological processes, sustains air and water resources, and contributes to the health and quality of life for America's communities and people."[21]

The green infrastructure concept indicates a planned network of green spaces that benefits wildlife and people, as opposed to just the leftover green bits that escape development. The word "infrastructure" implies that the green areas are critical to the functioning of a community or region and deserving of government funds. Similar to the built, or "gray," infrastructure, such as sewers and utilities, the green infrastructure also requires maintenance. Green infrastructure is not just about setting aside green space; it also helps frame the most-efficient location for development and growth of traditional gray infrastructure. Green infrastructure planning can happen at a variety of scales (local, regional, and statewide) and within different **land use** patterns (urban, suburban, rural, and wilderness).

Green Corridors

Connections and corridors, both for wildlife and humans, hold special significance within the green infrastructure concept. To help link green space, a community might prioritize the protection of a local stream corridor that links two existing green areas over a third discrete and isolated green patch. Corridors greatly expand our recreation possibilities and use of green space. One organization, the Rails-to-Trails Conservancy, seeks to enrich America's communities and countryside by creating a nationwide network of public trails from former rail lines.

A key tenet of conservation biology is preserving and connecting green spaces and corridors to allow wildlife and plant populations to flow, migrate, and find the resources they need to survive and reproduce. As the landscape becomes more and more fragmented, wildlife species that require large areas to roam, such as carnivores and large mammals, are increasingly imperiled. To help conserve biodiversity, at least some of our green spaces need to contain large tracts of undisturbed habitat. By preserving and connecting green spaces such as parks and natural areas with corridors, we can provide richer communities for both our human and our wildlife residents.

Tough Path Ahead

Despite the numerous benefits of green space and the increasing awareness of its importance, the challenge to conserve such space in light of growing human populations will not be easy. The costs associated with green space conservation require careful planning, dedicated resources, political will, and community support. It is often easier in the short term to move forward with development without considering the long-term implications of diminishing open space. As discussed throughout this module, growth is a necessary part of our communities' future. The challenge is not to stop growth but to channel it intelligently into the most appropriate areas while considering the needs of future generations of humans and wildlife.

In this activity, students will explore state and local communities that have taken action to protect their valuable green space in the face of development pressures.

Endnotes

1 U.S. Census Bureau Urban and Rural Population by State 2000 (E).
2 American Forests 2001 (E).
3 Ibid.
4 Dwyer et al. 2000 (E).
5 Wong 1999 (B).
6 Smith 1999 (E).
7 American Forests 2002 (E).
8 American Farmland Trust 2002 (C).
9 Smart Growth Network/ICMA 2002 (C).
10 Benfield, Raimi, and Chen 1999 (A).
11 City of Boulder 2003 (E).
12 Land Trust Alliance 2002 (E).
13 Lerner and Poole 1999 (C).
14 Urban Resources Initiative 2003 (E).
15 Lyman 2002 (E).
16 Smart Growth Network/ICMA 2002 (C).
17 Kuo and Sullivan 2001 (B).
18 Lerner and Poole 1999 (C).
19 Lerner and Poole 1999 (C).
20 Maryland Department of Natural Resources 2001 (E).
21 GreenInfrastructure.Net 2002a (E).

Letters following author and date citations refer to sections in the bibliography (Appendix B) where the reader can find full data about the sources cited.

Getting Ready

- Make copies of the following student pages: "Tall Tree Tales," "Greening Baltimore One Block at a Time," "Earth & Sky: Up on the Roof," "Green Inventory," and "Green Maryland—Connecting the Dots."
- Locate one or more aerial photographs of your area. See Appendix C for tips on finding aerial photographs. (*Note*: If you live in an area with deciduous trees, try to find a photo taken when leaves are on the trees.) If possible, make a photocopy or print out the photo for each team.
- To help identify community features, students may find that a local street or community map can be valuable.
- Contact your local government offices to find a current population estimate for your town or city, as well as information on projected growth rates. You can find recent population estimates for your town on the U.S. Census Bureau website. Visit Factfinder.census.gov, and enter your town's name in the "Basic Facts" section. Or use an older population estimate, and calculate an estimated growth rate yourself.

Doing the Activity

Part A

1. Distribute copies of the student page "Tall Tree Tales" to your students. Give the class a few minutes to complete the quiz.

2. Review the quiz. All the statements are true according to studies investigating the benefits of trees and open space. Discuss how the students categorized the nature of the statements – reflecting aesthetic, economic, ecological, health, and/or social concerns. You may want to point out that some statements apply to more than one category, which helps illustrate multiple reasons to conserve trees and green space. Encourage your students to also think of some of the drawbacks or challenges of preserving trees and green space. Below are possible answers.

1. S, A	2. H, $	3. H, A, S	4. E, H	5. S
6. E, $	7. E	8. S, A, $	9. $, H, E	10. E, $, H
11. H, E	12. H, $	13. $, A	14. E	15. E, $
16. $, A	17. H, S, A	18. H	19. E, $	20. H, S

A – Aesthetic $ – Economic S – Social
E – Ecological H – Health

3. Share a definition of the urban forest with your students (see the "Background" section in this activity). Distribute copies of "Greening Baltimore One Block at a Time." This case study offers an example of a community-based effort to green neighborhoods, plant trees, and give new life to abandoned lots.

4. After students read the case study and answer the questions, review and analyze students' responses as a class.

5. Ask students what they typically find on the roof of a building. Responses may include equipment, decks, etc. Some may respond with plants or gardens. Ask them to list the benefits of growing plants on a roof. Distribute copies of the "Earth & Sky: Up on the Roof" Student Page. The interview describes some of the ecological values of plants in reducing urban environmental problems. Use the Earth & Sky website for further information on the topic. Have the students use this information when completing the inventory in Part B below.

Part B

6. Ask students these questions: How green is your community? Where can you go to play sports? To bike or run? To watch birds? To relax outside in summer? What sorts of green resources are available in the community? Do community members use these areas? If they don't, why not?

7. Share with your students the definition of green infrastructure (see "Background"). Together, list the types of areas that might form a community's green infrastructure, such as natural areas (e.g., wetlands, woodlands, waterways, and wildlife habitat); public and private conservation lands (e.g., nature preserves,

wildlife corridors, greenways, and parks); public and private working lands that have conservation value (e.g., forests, tree farms, farms, and ranches); and outdoor recreation and trail networks.

8. Distribute copies of the student page "Green Inventory." Explain to students that, in teams of two or three, they will inventory the community's green infrastructure and draw a map. (*Note*: Students might choose to work with or create computer-generated maps.) If possible, encourage students to cover different areas of the community. For example, each team might cover several blocks. (For information on maps, please see Appendix C or the student page titled "Maps and Map Features" in Activity 3.)

9. Back in class, review and share "Green Inventory" results. As part of the discussion, encourage teams to share their estimates of the percentage of the survey area that is covered by green infrastructure.

10. To gain a different and broader perspective on the green infrastructure in your community, look with your students at an aerial photograph of your area (see Appendix C for tips on finding aerial photos). See if students can locate the areas that they surveyed. Identify the green infrastructure on the map, and discuss students' impressions. Is there more or less green and open space than they expected? Ask students how looking at this type of image helps them identify green infrastructure and gain a big-picture perspective. *Note*: If your students have completed the "Mapping Your Community through Time" in Activity 3, add the Green Infrastructure Team's findings.

11. Discuss whether or not the green spaces are well connected in your community. For example, could a squirrel or other local wildlife species make it from one green space to the next? Could a biker or runner travel a green path between areas? Are the areas large enough to meet the needs of a diversity of wildlife?

12. Share an estimate of your town's or city's human population with the class. Either provide an expected rate of growth over the next 10 years, or encourage students to calculate the growth rate using two data points (e.g., current and 10 years previous).
• How many more people will your community need to accommodate during the next 10 years?
• Where will they live? Shop? Work? Play?
• Where will this development likely be concentrated?
• Where should it occur?
• Do you think your community will be able to promote green space conservation in light of development pressures?
• What can be done?

Part C

13. Hand out copies of "Green Maryland— Connecting the Dots." This case study illustrates how Maryland has actively committed to linking green space in the state and to protecting green infrastructure that benefits both people and wildlife. While "Greening Baltimore One Block at a Time" describes a local initiative, this case study takes a broader look at a statewide approach to promoting green health. (For links to other case studies that could be used here, visit www.plt.org.)

14. After students have read the case study, ask them to respond to the accompanying questions in small groups or as a class.

15. Encourage students to reexamine the aerial photo of their community in light of the Maryland case study. Are linkages in place? Where are they needed? What is and is not possible? Where might new green spaces be created?

Enrichment

- Plant new trees in your community and help protect existing ones! Helpful resources are:

  – Envision Utah's publication, *Urban Planning Tools for Quality Growth:* www.envisionutah.org;

  – the National Arbor Day Foundation, www.arborday.org/arborday;

  – and American Forests' Global ReLeaf program, www.americanforests.org/our-programs/global-releaf-projects.

- Planting trees might be a GreenWorks! opportunity (www.plt.org).

- Encourage other members of the community to join (and perhaps help fund) your initiatives. Be sure to seek appropriate guidance from experts about tree selection, placement, and planting. Also, find out if your town has a tree ordinance and requirements. Work with local industry and the Wildlife Habitat Council to establish wildlife habitat in industrial areas.

- Invite a local forester, arborist, landscape architect, or nursery worker into your class to speak with students about trees in the community, plans for the future, and career options. If you plan to plant trees, those experts can be a wonderful resource and can answer students' questions.

- Have students estimate the percentage of your community with tree coverage as they examine an aerial photo or other resources. American Forests recommends that metropolitan areas strive for an overall tree cover of 40 percent (30 percent in the arid Southwest). Although local conditions vary, a city could achieve the recommended number with 15 percent coverage in downtown areas, 25 percent in urban residential and light commercial areas, and 60 percent in suburban residential area (www.americanforests.org).

- Instruct the students to work as a class to create an overall "green map" for their community, noting the different green areas, as well as their recreational and ecological benefits. Tell students to draw on resources from the town and organizations that manage local parks, nature preserves, and other green spaces. Student teams can be responsible for different areas and can engage in a variety of activities, including conducting site visits, interviewing staff, and writing up short blurbs about their respective areas. The Green Map System's website: www.greenmap.com, is a valuable source of information and offers models of green maps designed by kids.

- Consider purchasing *CITYgreen* as a technology extension. Students can use this innovative GIS software package to map urban ecology and measure the economic benefits of trees, soils, and other natural resources. For more information, visit: www.americanforests.org. Encourage students to survey community residents or schoolmates regarding their use of green space, current views on the intersection of growth and green space, and ideas about future trends and needs.

Tall Tree Tales

Circle T (true) or F (false) next to each statement below. Then, next to each statement, write the appropriate symbol(s) to indicate the nature of that statement:

A = Aesthetic, $ = Economic, E = Ecological, H = Health, and S = Social.

T F **1.** Trees increase the natural beauty of an area and make cities more livable.

T F **2.** The presence of nature and parks helps ensure regular physical activity, which can reduce the risk of coronary heart disease, hypertension, colon cancer, osteoporosis, arthritis, and diabetes.

T F **3.** Seeing green prevents people from being mean (i.e., it lowers their levels of aggression). One study found that apartment buildings with high levels of greenery had 56 percent fewer violent crimes than apartment buildings with little or no greenery.

T F **4.** The number of rats increases as tree coverage decreases.

T F **5.** More trees and grass in the common spaces of neighborhoods lead to better relationships between neighbors.

T F **6.** Trees slow and absorb storm water and reduce runoff, thereby reducing flooding and stream degradation. The job done by trees for free in the Seattle area would cost $2.4 billion if it were part of a storm water management system.

T F **7.** Generally speaking, the larger a park, forest, or nature preserve, the more diverse the *species* of wildlife and plants it will contain.

T F **8.** Prisons that incorporate some element of nature—even just a pleasant view—show higher rehabilitation rates.

T F **9.** Trees can lower the temperature of a city by 6–10 degrees. They can thus reduce energy use and even save lives during heat waves.

T F **10.** Tree leaves filter air pollutants. In large cities, those green filters are worth tens of millions of dollars in air pollution abatements each year.

T F **11.** One acre of trees provides enough oxygen to support 18 people.

T F **12.** Green settings can help relieve the symptoms of attention deficit disorder (ADD).

T F **13.** Trees can add from 7 percent to 20 percent to a home's value.

T F **14.** Habitat fragmentation is the greatest worldwide threat to forest wildlife and the primary cause of species extinction.

T F **15.** An average tree can absorb 26 pounds of carbon dioxide (the primary greenhouse gas) each year.

T F **16.** Across the nation, our parks, protected rivers, scenic lands, wildlife habitat, and recreational open space help support a $502 billion tourism industry.

T F **17.** Green views and access to green spaces can help urban residents cope with the stresses of daily activities.

T F **18.** Patients whose hospital rooms overlook trees require less pain medication and recover more quickly than those whose rooms overlook brick walls.

T F **19.** New York City has spent or committed $1.5 billion to protect the source of its water, a mostly forested watershed, rather than building a $10 billion filtration plant.

T F **20.** Tree-lined streets have the effect of reducing driving speeds, thus making neighborhoods safer for bikes and pedestrians.

Sources: American Forests 2005 (E). Carnegie Mellon University 1995 (C). Envision Utah 2003 (E). GreenInfrastructure.Net 2005 (E). Lerner and Poole 1999 (C). Lyman 2002 (E). Maryland Department of Natural Resources 2001 (E). University of Illinois Human–Environment Research Laboratory 2005 (E).

Case Study: Greening Baltimore One Block at a Time

Did you know that nearly one-quarter of the nation's trees are found in urban forests?

Why are urban forests important? Around the world, the role of urban forestry in creating "healthy" or "livable" cities tends to be underestimated. In addition to bestowing environmental benefits, planting and nurturing community trees can also address a full range of urban social issues, from illegal disposal to education to apathy to crime.

If you canvassed the city of Baltimore, Maryland, you might find as many as 40,000 vacant lots covering approximately 11 percent of the city's land area. About 12,000 of those lots fall under some type of city ownership. The lots represent a social, economic, and visual burden to the city. In many communities, they are dumped on, vandalized, and seen as a social blight rather than as a community benefit.

What Can Be Done?

Community greening can help turn abandoned land into community-owned property through the adoption (formal or informal) of vacant lands by local residents. The lots can be given new life as parks, community gardens, tree nurseries, or cultural gardens. When urban lands look used and cared for, people usually stop their dumping and curtail their littering. A city might spend between $2,000 and $4,000 per year to clean up just one problem lot. Yet greening can keep lots clean for a one-time investment of between $200 and $1,000 per lot.

Parks & People

Since 1984, the nonprofit foundation Parks & People has worked to enhance the health and beauty of Baltimore's communities and parks and to improve the quality of life for residents in Baltimore's neighborhoods. It encourages communities to take advantage of the city's valuable natural assets. Parks & People seeks to improve the physical, social, and environmental quality of neighborhoods through greening activities and by forming community networks to sustain natural resources.

Parks & People's Community Forestry Program helps Baltimore residents green their neighborhoods by offering educational opportunities and technical assistance to create parks and gardens in community open spaces and schoolyards and along neighborhood streets. The staff supports the planning, organizing, and implementing of greening projects in partnership with residents, city agencies, community associations, and other groups. Since 1993, more than 200 vacant lots have been transformed into community-managed parks or gardens. More than 7,000 promising new trees are growing in 45 Baltimore neighborhoods.

Enabling Funds

Parks & People's Community Grants Program awards up to $1,000 to Baltimore community groups that are interested in conducting neighborhood restoration projects such as tree plantings, community gardens, neighborhood cleanups, or environmental education activities. The grants finance tools, plant material, equipment, and other supplies. Since 1996, 403 community greening projects have been funded. Some of the grants support initiatives to build connectors to the Gwynns Falls Trail, a 14-mile hiking and biking trail that is still under development and will connect 24 neighborhoods and more than 2,000 acres of parkland, recreational facilities, and historic and cultural attractions.

What to Plant Where?

Educational opportunities include hands-on training in tree planting and pruning, soil testing, and streetscaping techniques. Classes are held four times a year on the following topics: developing greening projects and

Case Study: Greening Baltimore One Block at a Time (cont.)

funding strategies, plus volunteer recruitment, implementation, and maintenance. Volunteer community activists become Tree Tribers, who work throughout the city while training others to plant trees and to clean and green neighborhoods. The Tree Tribe Training Program provides hours of useful training in plant physiology, urban ecology, community assessment, and vacant lot improvement.

Parks & People also offers an environmental education program called KidsGrow, which is for children who are 7 to 13 years old. The program runs after school and throughout the summer, training kids to become activists in their own neighborhoods.

Other Successes

Parks & People has also developed green initiatives in housing areas that have been rehabilitated. In one such neighborhood, the community planted small trees in barrels outside doors. This action strengthened neighborhood ties and sparked similar efforts in the five surrounding blocks.

Greening in Baltimore has also been used as a catalyst to help communities fight crime. On one block, a tree planting effort led to a block watch, which led to a group called "pooches on patrol." In another neighborhood, residents organized a tree planting at night to send the message to potential drug dealers that the community cared.

Efforts to green Baltimore have made a difference. Greening improves residents' neighborhoods, health, and quality of life; as trees and gardens grow, so do those benefits. Community greening is more than just an interesting beautification strategy—it can be a vital part of any urban revitalization effort.

Source:
Adapted from Community Resource 2002 (E) and Parks & People 2002 (E).

Questions to Consider:
- What are some benefits of greening a city? What are the costs?
- How do you think Baltimore finds enough volunteers to make this program possible?
- If you ran the community greening program, what would you do differently?
- How can a community sustain this type of program?

Earth & Sky: Up on the Roof

How can cities become more green? Discover how Washington D.C. and other urban areas are changing their landscaping and designing more sustainable urban ecosystems.

Cities Ally With Nature to Solve Problems

From: *Earth & Sky Radio Series Program*
       August 21, 2005

JB: This is Earth and Sky. In places like cities, ecologists are looking at ways to maximize the ability of nature to provide us with essential services like clean air and water.

DB: At the moment, paved areas and rooftops of a city often cause real problems with water quality. Water that runs off over pavement gets to rivers and streams very quickly, and this water often carries pollution. Most storm gutter systems only remove water from property, but current systems do little to filter water.

JB: To comply with tougher water quality regulations, some urban areas like those around Washington D.C. are changing their landscaping — and designing more sustainable urban ecosystems. For example, "rain gardens" can be placed near buildings or in parking lots specifically to absorb and filter runoff. "Green roofs" accomplish the same thing with lightweight plants on rooftops. Margaret Palmer is a stream ecologist with the University of Maryland. She talked with us about using nature as an ally in solving environmental problems.

Palmer: Nature can do a lot of things for us if we're clever about thinking about some of those solutions... And in general, the rule of thumb is, the less engineered the solution, the more likely it is to cause fewer problems in the environment, and also to be less costly.

DB: With thanks today to the National Fish and Wildlife Foundation, we're Block and Byrd for Earth and Sky.

Author(s): Jorge Salazar

Earth & Sky
RADIO SERIES

The Earth & Sky radio series and website can be found at www.earthsky.org. The programs are produced by a non-profit organization committed to describing humans' work to understand themselves and their relationship to the Earth. The information in the Earth & Sky website, and in the daily radio series, is developed from interviews with scientists. This information is supported with additional resources on their website.

Project Learning Tree has worked with Earth & Sky to provide additional resources for many of the radio shows. See www.earthsky.org and www.plt.org

Green Inventory

Survey Team Members:

_____

_____

_____

_____

What kinds of green infrastructure can you find in your survey area? For example, can you find trees, parks, gardens, fields, cemeteries, streams, wetlands, rooftop gardens, and natural woodlands? What else?

Either on the back of this page or on a separate piece of paper, create a map of your survey area, illustrating the green infrastructure. Label the map clearly and create a legend. You don't need to draw every tree, but you might use a tree icon to depict a wooded area. Do your best to draw to scale, which will help show what percentage of the land is developed and what percentage is green space. If you spot any wildlife, mark it on your map.

After you create your map, answer the following questions:

1. What is the location of your survey area?

2. What do you estimate as the percentage of your survey area that is green infrastructure?

3. What do you estimate as the percentage of your survey area that is developed?

4. Do you think your community's green infrastructure is growing or shrinking? Why?

5. How much do you think the habitat has changed for native wildlife over the past 100 years?

6. Does your community's green infrastructure enhance its visual character?

7. In your opinion, does your community have enough green infrastructure?

8. How much of the green infrastructure consists of mostly native species?

9. Are there any noxious weeds or invasive species?

10. How can you use the inventory to implement a greening project?

11. Did this inventory affect your sense of place? If so, how? If not, why not? Do you think your sense of place would change if green space increased or decreased in the future? Why?

Case Study: Green Maryland—Connecting the Dots

Consider the following:
- Before European colonization, 95 percent of Maryland was carpeted by green forest. By 1993, forest area had decreased to 47 percent of the state's land area.
- Maryland has lost 50 percent of its pre-settlement wetlands.
- Between 1790 and 1990, Maryland's population grew from 320,000 to 4,780,000 people.
- At least 180 plant species and 35 animal species have been eliminated from Maryland, including elk, gray wolves, bison, and mountain lions. Another 310 plant species and 165 animal species are rare, threatened, or endangered.

Is it too late for Maryland to take action to protect its rich ecosystems and wild treasures? Is there hope for maintaining a balance between the needs of humans and the needs of wild species?

Recently, Maryland has been working hard to strike a balance between the natural and built environments and to find innovative methods to accommodate growth while still protecting the best features of Maryland.

Greenways

In 1990, a Maryland executive order established the Maryland Greenways Commission, with the goal of providing a statewide natural infrastructure by protecting and connecting important natural corridors throughout the state. Since then, Maryland has protected more than 1,500 miles of greenways corridors, including more than 600 miles of land trails and 300 miles of water trails. Consequently, the state is a national leader in efforts to preserve a network of natural corridors that connect areas of open space.

Greenways are natural corridors that have been set aside to connect larger areas of open space and to provide for the conservation of natural resources, including city water supplies, protection of habitats, and movement of plants and animals. Greenways also offer opportunities for linear recreation like bike trails, alternative transportation, and nature study. The Maryland Greenways program works with local governments, citizen groups, land trusts, businesses, and private organizations.

What Types of Corridors?

Among the corridors in the greenways system are trails along rivers, streams, ridgelines, abandoned rail lines, and wild vegetated corridors. To be considered part of the statewide greenways network, land must be under some form of permanent protection and serve at least one of several greenways functions:
- Riparian and water quality protection
- Wildlife and ecological corridors
- Linear shaped parks (can be natural areas or developed recreation sites)
- Trails (as long as they include a significant vegetated buffer).

All Maryland greenways provide some ecological benefits, and most serve multiple purposes. For example, parks along stream valleys, especially in urban areas, tend to take on multiple functions such as buffers, flood control, wildlife corridors, and recreation. Most corridors, however, can be classified as primarily ecological or recreational. Most of the current land is publicly owned, but numerous easements are being placed on private properties to enhance the growing network of corridors.

The Baltimore and Annapolis Trail exhibits a green corridor. It is an established recreational greenway following the route of the old Baltimore and Annapolis Railroad. The linear park connects two towns, stretches 13.3 miles, and covers 112 acres. The trail has a 10-foot-wide paved surface within a 66-foot-wide landscaped corridor. Walkers, runners, bicyclists, equestrians, and various forms of wildlife all use the trail.

Case Study: Green Maryland—Connecting the Dots (cont.)

Sample Map

As part of the project, an atlas of greenways, water trails, and green infrastructure was created. For each county in the state, the greenways maps show protected lands, including those owned by a conservation or government agency, those owned or under easement to a land trust, and those under agricultural easements. The maps also depict existing, planned, and potential greenways corridors. To see a sample map for Baltimore County, visit this link: http://dnr.maryland.gov/greenways/introduction.html.

The GreenPrint Program

The sample map of Baltimore County and other maps in the atlas illustrate that Maryland has protected green space. Yet, is it enough? Maryland has only two million acres of ecologically significant land that has not been consumed by development. Of these two million acres of "green infrastructure," almost three-fourths are unprotected. Billions of dollars are spent each year to construct or maintain the state's built infrastructure of roads, bridges, and utilities that residents depend on. By contrast, the state's green infrastructure, which exists naturally, is under tremendous development pressure. Without protection, the remaining green infrastructure is vulnerable and subject to further loss and fragmentation.

So how is Maryland increasing its protection of the state's green infrastructure? Protecting land requires money. In May 2001, the governor signed into law a new $35 million GreenPrint program as a major expansion to the Greenways program. GreenPrint aims to help protect Maryland's most-valuable remaining ecological lands and the state's long-term ecological health.

The program follows a three-step process:
1. Identifying the most important unprotected natural lands in the state by using the most up-to-date computer mapping techniques
2. Linking, or connecting, those lands through a system of corridors or connectors
3. Saving those lands through targeted acquisitions and easements

The program will support efforts to steer growth to appropriate areas while preserving portions of the landscape that make Maryland both bountiful and captivating.

Green Infrastructure Assessment

A Green Infrastructure Assessment is an essential component of the program to help identify and prioritize areas in need of conservation and restoration. It has focused on two types of important resource lands: "green hubs" and "green links." Green hubs form the heart of Maryland's green infrastructure and typically span hundreds of acres. The hubs serve a vital function in maintaining the state's vibrant and unique ecology. Green hubs are connected by green links—ribbons of land such as stream valleys and mountain ridge lines that function as "habitat highways." The habitat highways allow safe passage for wildlife through their natural domain; facilitate seed and pollen transport, which helps plant life thrive across the state; and keep streams and wetlands healthy by protecting adjacent vegetation. Preserving linkages between the remaining large habitat areas will ensure the long-term survival and continued diversity of Maryland's natural resources and environment.

Case Study: Green Maryland—Connecting the Dots (cont.)

Who Gains from the Program?

The GreenPrint program affects all Maryland citizens. For some people, like those who harvest and process timber, it affects their jobs. The program supports Maryland's economy, especially forest products, seafood, and tourism. For other people, the green infrastructure provides places for hobbies, recreational activities, and learning opportunities. Nature lovers can enjoy hiking, camping, observing, and photographing a wide variety of plants and animals.

Developers, private landowners, and others will benefit from having a clear understanding of where the most ecologically valuable lands are located and where targeted conservation activities will be directed. Local governments will be able to enhance their efforts to provide open space, recreation lands, and natural areas that retain the unique character of their communities and rural landscapes. The GreenPrint program helps preserve and safeguard Maryland's rich quality of life and its special natural landscapes, such as picturesque, rolling mountains; forest lands and wooded wetlands; expansive native marshes; and the Chesapeake Bay. Action taken today will help ensure that future generations have the same opportunities to enjoy Maryland's outstanding natural resources and high quality of life as residents do today.

Sources:
Maryland Department of Natural Resources (E).
Smart Growth Network/ICMA 2002 (C).

Questions to Consider:

- How did Maryland identify high-priority lands to target conservation efforts?
- What do you think are the most important components of Maryland's plans?
- Does this program favor or discourage growth? Explain.
- Do you think the program will succeed? Why or why not? Which criteria would you use to determine success?
- Does your state have a similar program?
- Do you think this program would be funded in a tight budget year? Why or why not?

Notes

6

A Vision for the Future

Student teams develop and present a vision for the future of an area in their community.

Subjects
Environmental Studies, Social Studies

Concepts
1.6 Successful technologies are those that are appropriate to the efficient and sustainable use of resources, and to the preservation and enhancement of environmental quality.

3.11 Effective citizen involvement in the environmental decision-making process involves a careful study of all sides of the issues, along with the ability to differentiate between honest, factually accurate information and propaganda.

4.6 Human-built environments, if planned, constructed, and landscaped to be compatible with the environment in which they will be located, can conserve resources, enhance environmental quality, and promote the comfort and well-being of those who will live within them.

Skills
Analyzing, Comparing and Contrasting, Comprehending, Decision Making, Determining Causes and Effects, Identifying Main Ideas, Problem Solving, Summarizing, Synthesizing and Creating.

Materials
Copies of a case study (either from the student pages or from PLT's website at www.plt.org) and copies of student pages, two paper squares or stars (or something similar) of two different colors for each group of four or five students, paper, markers

Time Considerations
Three or four 50-minute periods

Objectives
▶ Students will discover how a community has responded to the challenge of managing growth.

▶ Students will follow the four basic steps of the "Oregon Model" to create a vision for a selected area of their local community.

▶ Students will identify the elements that they consider important for a good quality of life.

▶ Students will explore how they can turn their vision into a plan for action.

Assessments
▶ Ask students to develop a media release or newspaper article about their visioning process. The piece should describe the processes, challenges, and results and should tell how it could affect the future. Consider sharing the results with real community outlets such as the school or town newspaper.

▶ Ask students to design a one-page flyer inviting citizens to attend a mock community-visioning meeting. The best flyers will be clear, concise, and compelling. They should appeal to a wide audience, provide an overview of the visioning process, articulate why visioning is important, and motivate people to become involved.

▶ Hold a mock community-visioning meeting with students debating the plans from the viewpoints of various characters (e.g., mayor, student, member of a conservation organization, housing developer).

▶ Have students design an instrument that could be used to evaluate the community's progress in reaching the goals outlined in the class's vision. What are the measurable and observable criteria that will indicate whether the community is moving toward its goals?

Background

I know of no safe depository of the ultimate power of society but the people themselves, and if we think them not enlightened enough to exercise their control with a wholesome discretion, the remedy is not to take it from them, but to inform their discretion by education.

–Thomas Jefferson

Do you know how your neighborhood will look in 20 years? What vision and plans does your community have in place to shape its future? The pressures to accommodate growing human needs and wants exert significant strain on our communities and the natural environment, challenging us to reexamine how we plan our communities. Like it or not, growth is on our local, national, and global agendas. Among the challenges we face today are managing growth, deciding in our communities what is necessary and what is unnecessary growth, and accommodating growth within limits imposed by certain conditions, such as limited water supplies. Collectively, we need to draw on lessons from the past, to find ways to balance human needs with the needs of the rest of the planet, and to seek innovative solutions that will leave our children with well-planned, livable, functional communities.

How do communities make decisions concerning **land use**? How can competing interests be resolved? For example, how does a community reconcile the desire to boost the local economy by building office space to attract businesses versus the desire to avoid increasing automobile traffic on area roads, or the desire to have convenient **big-box stores** without driving out established local stores? How can communities balance the need to develop land with the need to protect **green space**, air, water, **scenic** quality, and our natural ecosystems?

Who Is Planning Your Community's Future?

Decisions concerning land use are among the most important—and contentious—that our nation's communities will make over the next several decades. Citizens throughout the country—including current and prospective homeowners, local and state government officials, developers, architects, designers and planners, farmers, and business leaders—all have a share in land use choices. Many of the decisions that people make today will affect the future. For instance, a seemingly small and private decision to sell a family farm to a housing developer has lasting repercussions on the family's future generations, their neighbors, the community's **visual character**, and the **watershed** and ecology of the area. The way in which we use our land resources today will influence the cleanliness of our air, the purity of our water, and the health of our ecosystems for years to come.

Other influential land use decisions that will affect our future are made at the community level. For example, town officials might decide whether or not to allow a new development or whether or not to incorporate low-income housing. Modern state planning laws typically require (or encourage) local governments to develop land use plans. **Comprehensive management plans**, or master plans, describe the type of development that a community would like to have, the level of service and infrastructure that it will offer, and the values that a community wishes to create or maintain.

Comprehensive plans establish goals and strategies that address transportation, economic development, **affordable housing**, community infrastructure, open space preservation, and water resource protection, among other interests. Land use plans allow communities to evaluate development projects in terms of local and regional priorities, thus reducing the incidence of haphazard development. Public policy requirements, such as planning and **zoning** laws, can help expand or limit a community's land use choices. A community vision—a long-range set of goals and guidelines that describe the type of community the locality would like to become in the future—is typically one component of a comprehensive plan.

A Vision and a Plan...

How do we chart a course for the future? Two widely used tools are planning and **visioning**. Both terms are often used loosely and in a number of contexts. Communities plan in both the short and long term. The scale of community planning also varies considerably: one planning meeting might focus on the location of a new public pool, while another might focus on developing a strategic plan to help an entire city achieve agreed-upon goals by the year 2030. In all cases, planning relates to thinking about the future. (See Activity 4 "Neighborhood Design" for more information on planning.)

Visioning generally goes one step further. The term "visioning" describes a process in which participants set aside their preconceptions of what's possible and, instead, imagine

improvements that they would personally like to see happen to create a better future. Focusing on what people see as *desirable*, rather than on what they think is *possible*, can generate a creative atmosphere in which new ideas emerge and people's goals can be revealed. Proponents of this technique argue that it is only by encouraging people to talk about their underlying aspirations that an open discussion can then take place. More and more communities are using visioning as a way to plan for their future. As with planning, visioning can happen at many different scales. For example, a small town might create a vision for a new local park, or several communities might come together to develop a vision for a region that spans several counties.

Visioning in Action

Many styles and models exist for visioning. For example, the state of Oregon has been a pioneer in visioning and has developed a model used in many other parts of the country. The student activity that follows in this section most closely follows the Oregon Model, which asks four basic questions:

- Where are we now?
- Where are we going?
- Where do we want to be?
- How do we get there?

Yet, communities that follow prescribed models are not the only ones engaged in a form of visioning. Visioning can also be less formal or can involve different steps and approaches. What different models of visioning have in common, however, is a process of taking stock of where a community is headed and working toward a better future. Visioning alone does not help a community achieve its vision. A critical step that a community must take is to develop an action plan (or "strategic" plan), which might include specific projects, timelines, assignments of responsibilities, costs, and milestones to help monitor progress and achieve desired goals. In some models, including the Oregon Model, developing the action plan is an integrated component of the visioning process. Therefore, in the end, both visioning and planning work in concert with each other to help a community move toward a desired outcome.[1]

Are You Involved?

Community planning is not exclusively the domain of elected officials, outside consultants, and developers. Everyone is responsible for helping to plan his or her community's future. In fact, any community's most important resource for creating its vision for the future is its citizens.[2] Granted, this concept is not always easy. Many people are caught up in the rush of day-to-day life and may feel too busy to dedicate time and energy to planning how their neighborhood might look in 20 years. Yet, if we don't think about what we want our communities to become or what we would like to preserve or change, then who will represent the needs of local residents? In some cases, the integrity of our communities might be altered—almost imperceptibly—until one day we wake up and see the far-reaching consequences of those accumulated small changes. In other cases, we might leave decisions about what's best for our neighborhoods and cities up to outside developers or state or federal agencies that are located hundreds of miles away. Residents who don't actively play a role in shaping the future of their community may become victims of their future.[3]

Sometimes, people don't feel that they possess the skills or expertise to evaluate **land use planning** decisions or to become involved in community planning.

There are many benefits of involving youth in planning, including (1) empowering them to become credible and influential citizens; (2) offering an opportunity to explore urban, social, and civic studies; (3) inviting them to become active citizens by using the "learn-by-doing" method; and (4) encouraging them to analyze information, organize ideas, and communicate findings.[4] Furthermore, interested young people don't need to wait until they are adults to participate in land use planning. According to the Center for Rural Pennsylvania, a special effort should be made to include youth in community visioning because they can offer different viewpoints and can provide specific skills and talents that can contribute significantly to the visioning process. Involving youth can also help them to develop a greater sense of civic commitment and can encourage them to return to their communities after completing their education. This involvement is especially important in areas that have seen a large exodus because of the lack of opportunity. One goal of this activity is to help involve your students in an exciting, real-world project that will affect not only them, but also their children.

Endnotes

1 Ames 2001 (E).
2 Center for Rural Pennsylvania 2000 (E).
3 Ibid.
4 Race and Torma 1998 (A).

Letters following author and date citations refer to sections in the bibliography (Appendix B) where the reader can find full data about the sources cited.

Getting Ready

- Choose and photocopy a case study to share with your students (either from the student pages or from the other examples on PLT's website at www.plt.org).
- Photocopy the student pages "Visioning—Steps 1 and 2" and "Visioning—Steps 3 and 4."
- Make or find two paper squares or stars (or something similar) of two different colors for each group of four or five students.

Doing the Activity

1. Have the students work as a class to make a list of books, movies, cartoons, and other examples that depict how life will be in the future (such as *Futurama*, *The Jetsons*, *Brave New World*, *The Handmaids Tale*, *1984*, *The Matrix*, *12 Monkeys*, *A.I.*, *Waterworld*, and *Star Trek*). Go through the list, and have the students describe the visions of daily life provided by those works. Draw on the following questions to fuel your discussion. *Optional*: As an extension, have your students watch or read one of the aforementioned works and evaluate it.
- How do cities and neighborhoods look in terms of layout and design?
- Do the designs of the cities and neighborhoods include green space? Open space? Scenic views?
- How do people travel?
- How do people obtain their food and other necessities?
- How and where do people foster social bonds?
- What events or circumstances might have led to such a future?
- Do you think this future was planned? If so, by whom?
- Which world would you prefer to live in? Why?
- Which world do you think most closely represents our future? Why?

2. Break the class into small groups, and distribute copies of the case study you selected. Then explain that many people have visions for the future of their community. Instruct students to read the case study and to think about the following questions. *Note*: You may want to distribute a different case study to each small group, thus allowing students to compare and contrast different community visions.

3. Have the students discuss the following questions as a class or in small groups:
- What is the community's vision for the future?
- What inspired the community to chart a new course for its future?
- Who participated in the visioning process?
- Were young people involved in the planning? If not, how could they have been included?

- What tradeoffs would community members need to accept to achieve the vision?
- What would be the major outcomes if the vision were implemented?
- Which elements of the vision do you think will be the easiest and the hardest to implement?
- What do you consider the greatest strength and the greatest weakness of the plan? Why?
- Are any of the issues discussed in the case study relevant to your community?

4. Next, explain that students will do a visioning exercise for an area of their community. All students will focus on the same area. Mention that visioning goes beyond planning—visioning suggests that a community can design and create its own future. First, decide on the area—the school, park, shopping area, neighborhood, abandoned lot, or wetland. Wherever you and your students select, it is critical that the area be clearly defined. Think about areas that might be threatened by development, that are in need of attention, or that might be redesigned to be more youth-friendly. (Consider using one of the places that students chose for the student activity titled "Personal Places" or a neighborhood analyzed in the student activity titled "Neighborhood Design.") Pick an area that is complex enough to provide room for analysis and creativity but small enough to be manageable. For example, consider accessibility issues and available resources. If time allows, one of the most rewarding and relevant explorations can be creating a vision for the future of your entire neighborhood.

5. Explain that students will base their visioning efforts on the Oregon Model. Distribute copies of "Visioning—Steps 1 and 2," and briefly discuss these four guiding questions:
- Where are we now (i.e., the community profile)?
- Where are we going (i.e., the trend statement)?
- Where do we want to be (i.e., the vision statement)?
- How do we get there (i.e., the action plan)?

6. Divide the class into groups of four or five students, and tell them to follow the instructions in "Visioning—Steps 1 and 2." The groups will (1) explore the area in its current state and (2) imagine what the area will be like in 20 years on the basis of current trends. The product of each step will be a visual map of the area. Students might use cameras and sketches to assist them in their efforts.

7. Distribute copies of "Visioning—Steps 3 and 4." The third and fourth steps are the heart of the visioning process as groups design their idealized version of the future. This exercise culminates in the creation of a third map of the area.

8. Encourage the groups to take a few minutes to compare the products of steps 2 and 3.

9. Have students deliver their group presentations. As the groups present their community visions, the other members of the class will prepare questions to ask the presenters. After their presentations, the groups will leave their maps displayed around the classroom.

10. After all groups have presented, encourage each group to discuss and selects its favorite and second-favorite vision for the future. Provide each group with two different-colored squares or stars (explain which colors correspond to first and second choices). Have each group place its colored squares or stars on the chosen maps. *Note*: You might want to use secret ballots.

11. Discuss the following questions:
- How are the visions similar? Different?
- How does each vision express the group's desired quality of life?
- How do the different visions encourage a sense of place and support the needs of the community members?
- What did the students learn about what is important to someone else?
- What is the role of planning and design in making a vision a reality? Who can help?
- Is there a particular vision that the class could try to implement? Or are there components of different visions?
- Who might be able to help the students achieve their vision and learn how they can enlist such aid?

- Who might hinder the students in achieving their vision; and how can the students involve those parties more constructively?

12. Choose one or more aspects from the visions to implement as a service-learning project. Consider starting with a small, highly visible project. After choosing your project, develop a detailed action plan—the final step in the visioning process. Think about timelines, tasks to be accomplished, resources needed, people needed, budget, and assignment of responsibilities. You might divide your class into task forces to help accomplish components of the project. Be sure to document your progress, perhaps with photos, journals, sketches, or progress reports. What are the consequences of this single act? How did it make a difference? For more information about GreenWorks! grants for service-learning projects, see PLT's website at *www.plt.org*.

Enrichment

- Have your class follow these steps to help distill the top priorities from the groups' visions:
  - Members of each group decide on three top planning priorities for their community.
  - Serving as a facilitator, the teacher or an appointed student solicits the priorities from each group.
  - Groups present their priorities, trying to convince others of the value of their ideas.
  - The facilitator encourages discussion on the different items, and then seeks agreement from the class as a whole about the top five or six priorities.
- Computer integration. Have students use simulation, or "sims," types of programs or games. Evaluate students on the effectiveness of their "neighborhood." You could also have students design their own survey at *www.surveymonkey.com* and collect the

opinions of various community members. (The survey tool is free but requires users to register.)

- Two of the key components of community visioning are (1) integrating the input of as many members of the community as possible in developing the vision and (2) encouraging others to adopt and help implement a new vision. Encourage your students to find ways to share their ideas with others and to solicit their feedback. For example, students might want to invite guest speakers to share their insights and to offer technical advice, or they may want to develop a survey or stage a focus group to obtain input from others. Or, if your class developed a vision for the schoolyard, students might write a letter or meet with members of the school board to share their ideas. Also consider sharing some of your students' ideas about the future with local media channels, parents, or other groups. Students might plan an unveiling ceremony, a multimedia presentation, or a "town meeting" to solicit input from other members of the community. The web can be another important vehicle for spreading the word and possibly encouraging feedback.

Case Study: Loudoun County, Virginia

For hundreds of years Loudoun County, Virginia, has been characterized by green infrastructure (agricultural land, forests, streams, and mountainsides) and heritage resource assets (historic, prehistoric, and scenic sites). Those special attributes make the county an attractive place to live and contribute to the regional economy.

Loudoun County also finds itself conveniently located about 35 miles west of Washington, D.C., where it has become home to a growing number of businesses and people. By the 1990s, Loudoun County had been transformed into one of the fastest-growing counties in the nation. How much development can a rural community support and still retain its visual and cultural character? Loudoun County is still struggling to find out.

Background

Loudoun County was once a quiet, rural community dominated by vegetable and horse farms. Towns served as the centers of population and commerce, with land beyond their corporate limits planned for rural, residential, or agricultural uses. For 200 years, the population remained at approximately 20,000 residents. However, beginning in 1960, the county began to experience rapid change. Population growth in neighboring Fairfax County began to spill into Loudoun County. The expansion of sewer service in eastern Loudoun County and the opening in 1962 of Washington Dulles International Airport, which straddles Loudoun and Fairfax Counties, encouraged residential and commercial development—and helped to set a new course of growth for the county. Land around the airport was rezoned to accommodate airport-related businesses, which encouraged large companies to locate in the area, including two telecommunication giants in the 1990s: America Online and WorldCom. Businesses took advantage of the large tracts of relatively inexpensive, open land (also called "greenfields") to build large commercial complexes.

The new businesses helped to attract new residents, who, in turn, created the need for more housing options. During the 1960s and in each decade that followed, Loudoun County's population rose by at least 50 percent (see Figure 1). In 1950, the population of Loudoun County was 21,147. In 2000, that number had grown to 169,599. From 2000 to 2005, the population increased 46% to 247,293. Development in the county shifted from a more traditional rural style toward a suburban land use pattern that included new commercial shopping strips with big parking lots in front, houses with deep setbacks, and very long blocks. Farmland in the western part of the county began to be subdivided into three-acre residential lots. New residents demanded services, such as trash pickup, which had not been historically provided in the county.

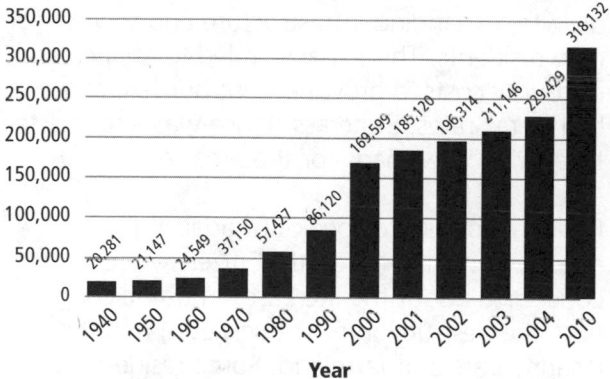

Figure 1 Loudoun County, Virginia, Population, 1940–2010

Source: U.S. Census Bureau, Loudoun County Department of Economic Development, and Loudoun County Fiscal Impact Committee 2004, (E).

During that time, Loudoun County also experienced tremendous commercial construction. From 1990 to 2000, more than 2,000 new companies, including several major employers, located in the county. Between 1991 and 2000, unemployment rates dropped from 3.5 percent to 0.09 percent.

Case Study: Loudoun County, Virginia (cont.)

Growing Pains

The rapid development of Loudoun County also brought a host of problems, including water quantity and quality issues. The increase in impervious land cover (i.e., asphalt and concrete) prevented rainwater from filtering through the soil and replenishing groundwater. In turn, this situation both diminished ground-water capacity and damaged streams. Culverts and other pipe systems transported water in much higher volumes and at much greater velocities than natural systems, causing erosion of stream banks. Stormwater runoff containing pollutants such as litter, road salt, oil, and metals then found its way into local waterways.

The county also faced transportation problems as rural roads and thoroughfares failed to meet increased demands. Commuters traveling to and from Loudoun County faced increased traffic delays.

Loudoun County struggled to keep up with its growth, expanding infrastructure and services for new residents. This expansion led to an increase in county costs, a growing debt burden, and higher tax rates. State assistance was also enlisted to provide new roads for the area.

Residents began to speak out against the negative effects of growth. Citizens were concerned about the increases in traffic conges-tion, the destruction of scenic views, and the disappearance of farmland. Some residents felt that uncontrolled development was destroy-ing the essence of what made the county a special place in which to live. They believed that if Loudoun County continued to develop at the current rate, it would become a less-desirable place and that real estate values would drop. Some homeowners resented having to pay additional property taxes to cover the cost of new services. Each new house cost the county more than $21,000 in school construction, public security, and other costs, and some residents felt that developers, who benefited most from the development, should help pay those costs.

A Smarter Approach

Loudoun residents began to advocate a smarter approach to growth. They felt that with improved planning, the county could preserve the farmland economy, help protect stream corridors, reduce traffic, safeguard the area's physical beauty, and maintain the community's character. Cluster or conservation design could maximize green space and protect watersheds by directing growth to compact neighbor-hoods in town centers or to other designated "growth" areas. Furthermore, controlling growth in the county could cut the number of new schools needed in half. (The 1991 County Plan predicted the need for 125 new schools; with proposed growth management changes, the county would need only 64 new schools.)

Some residents, however, were concerned that controlling growth would increase housing values and price lower-income residents out of the market. Private property rights advocates also opposed growth management measures, suggest-ing that zoning and growth control constituted an infringement of their rights. Some rural landown-ers also opposed new measures, wanting instead to retain the freedom to sell their land for profit. In November 1999, the citizens of Loudoun County voted out of office all but one member of the nine-member county board of supervi-sors, favoring the candidates who promoted slower growth. As a start, the new board voted to give the county more money for school

Case Study: Loudoun County, Virginia (cont.)

construction and the authority to limit building permits if government facilities were not in place to meet the needs of new residents. From 2000 to 2001, the citizens, the planning commission, the board of supervisors, the county staff, and the consultants worked to create an ambitious new vision for the county in its Revised Comprehensive Plan.

Community support would be vital to the plan's implementation and success, so the revised plan was prepared with extensive citizen involvement. The planning team made efforts to allow easy access to new information and to the planning process. For example, public notebooks containing relevant documents and information were placed in six public libraries and in the department of planning. The planning department also posted documents on its website. All sessions of the planning commission and board of supervisors were open to the public and recorded on audiotapes. In early 2000, the planning commission held three initial sessions for public input. Several months later, more than 450 people attended three planning forums and discussed the issues in a more interactive format. Focus groups on environmental implementation and on community design and identity were also part of the process. The planning team held a public input forum before the preparation of the draft. Subsequently, the planning commission conducted more than 17 hours of public hearings on the draft before a revised version was finally adopted on July 23, 2001.

The New Plan

Loudoun County's new plan revolved around the concept that "development should be systematic, in compact communities, and in the right location, in order to function well and to enable the county to provide adequate, and cost-efficient, public services." Key features of the county's new plan included the following:
- Identify and protect its "Green Infrastructure"—defined as the county's environmental, natural resource, and heritage features—through zoning for clustered lots, open space, and increased rural land uses.
- Establish separate areas for growth and areas to be protected for rural purposes. About 300 square miles, or about two-thirds of the county, would be preserved.
- Focus development in four traditional towns in the eastern part of the county that have town centers and mixed-use design features.
- Reduce the number of homes that can be built by 44 percent countywide.
- Increase rural land uses to enhance the rural economy.
- Alter zoning in the western part of the county to retain rural character. In the southwest, 1 home is permitted per 50 acres (or 1 home per 20 acres if development is clustered to save open space). In the northwest, 1 home is permitted per 20 acres (1 home per 10 acres if clustered). Those zoning policies will reduce new home construction from the proposed 187,000 to 110,000 houses. Before passage of the new plan, developers were able to build one house per 3 acres.
- Maintain the existing Purchase of Development Rights program, a voluntary incentive for property owners to keep their land as open space.
- Commit the county to evaluate future development proposals on the basis of its ability to treat and distribute a safe and adequate drinking water supply.
- Commit the county to strengthen its affordable housing policies.
- Concentrate the development of transportation systems in designated suburban growth areas and towns.
- Promote significant improvements to pedestrian and bicycle networks.
- Focus on other pedestrian-friendly features on streets.
- Require developers to provide a larger share of the capital facilities costs associated with residential construction.

Case Study: Loudoun County, Virginia (cont.)

Implementing the Plan

Loudoun County implemented its Revised Comprehensive Plan beginning in 2003. The board of supervisors adopted revisions to the county's zoning ordinance and a new zoning map. The county sought to maintain the rural character of western Loudoun by protecting it from suburban sprawl and by encouraging small-scale businesses such as inns, wineries, and retreats. The rationale was that growth should occur in existing communities in the eastern portion of the county. However, the new rules fueled controversy within the state and raised questions about the constitutionality and sensibility of the plan.

The policy did not seem to abate the county's economic problems. Residents feared that the strict regulations would increase housing prices. Some argued that the uncontrolled growth had put the county into debt and increased property taxes. Furthermore, nearly 200 lawsuits had been filed against the county, which had caused it to set aside $6 million to cover defense fees.

Residents worried that the policies would increase sprawl. The *Washington Post* backed that theory after examining policies designed to protect rural areas in 14 other counties in Maryland and Northern Virginia. In those counties, suburban sprawl actually increased because residents were forced to move away from urban areas in attempts to find affordable housing.

Members of the Loudoun County Board of Supervisors faced re-election in November 2003. The election had the potential of changing the leadership and even the nature of the smart growth policy. When the votes were counted the slow-growth politicians who had made up the Board of Supervisors were defeated. The election put an end to the "smart-growth" plan, and brought a board that followed more of a "market growth" approach. The board removed many of the growth restraints enacted by the previous board. This cleared the way for Loudoun County to have the third-fastest annual growth rate in the nation between 2003 and 2004 according to the U.S. Censes Bureau. The growth rate was an 8.1% population increase. The new board however, did not remove the restrictive zoning regulations in the western part of the county. During this period the county government was also given the green light for development to an already expanding business community. More jobs meant more people, which mean more schools, roads, and more office buildings.

In March of 2005, the Virginia Supreme Court declared the 2003 zoning law in the western part of the county invalid. The court ruled that the public was not given proper public notice concerning the zoning hearings and that the officials had not clearly specified the boundaries of the land that was to be rezoned. County planners hope a rewrite of the plan will be approved. According to a county planner, development in 2006 is nearly a free-for-all as builders rush to start projects before regulations are in place.

Today, residents struggle to identify the county's character and its future. One resident said, "What is Loudoun County? Are we a high-tech county? That didn't work. Are we rural? We don't want to be rural…. We're still trying to figure out what we want to be when we grow up."

Sources:
Davenport 2006 (B).
Laris 2003 (B).
Laris and Whoriskey 2001 (B).
Loudoun County Board of Supervisors 2005 (E).
Milligan 2003 (B).

Case Study: Livable Tucson Vision Program

What will the future be like in your neighborhood? Will your children inherit a healthy, vibrant community or one suffering from the legacy of poorly planned growth?

From Seattle to Jacksonville, communities across the country are starting to define a vision for their future that balances the needs of this generation without compromising the ability of future generations to meet their needs. Residents of "sustainable" cities are learning and demonstrating that balancing the economic, social, and environmental concerns of their communities can improve their quality of life and ensure a better future.

In the spring of 1997, the mayor and city council of Tucson, Arizona, initiated the Livable Tucson Vision Program to identify a long-term, community-driven vision for the city. That vision was created to help shape the city's budget and to provide a framework for developing programs and services that address the real concerns of the community.

More than 1,200 community members, business-people, and city employees have participated in the program to date, thereby laying the groundwork for developing new and enhanced programs and services that will help realize the community's vision of a more Livable Tucson.

Background

During the spring and summer of 1997, three public forums were held in each ward to engage the community in identifying a common vision and finding strategies for achieving a sustainable community. In addition to the ward forums, additional forums were held in the fall that targeted businesses, youth, and Spanish speakers. An Internet site also gave citizens the opportunity to contribute their priorities, and city council offices had bulletin boards for community input.

Based on thousands of comments voiced by the community, 17 key goals emerged. Those goals embodied the values and aspirations of the community to maintain and improve Tucson in the future. The next phase of the Livable Tucson Vision Program involved holding six workshops in the spring of 1998 to develop indicators of progress toward each of the 17 key goals. Taken together, the indicators form a community report card.

Livable Tucson Goals and Indicators

The 17 key goals and the areas that they address for a livable Tuscon are as follows:

- Better alternatives to automobile transportation—improved public transportation system, bicycle and pedestrian-friendly streets, improved roadways (with landscaping, lighting, sidewalks, and bus stops), and promotion of alternatives to the automobile
- Engaged community and responsive government—involvement of citizens in the community, volunteering, neighborhood participation, responsiveness of government organizations to citizen input, and the connection between government and the people

Case Study: Livable Tucson Vision Program (cont.)

- Safe neighborhoods—how safe people feel in their neighborhoods, crime, policing, and risk perceptions
- Caring, healthy families and youth—opportunities, services, and conditions that support Tucson's families and youth
- Excellent public education—the quality of education at all levels, youth to adult, as well as vocational, life skills, cultural, and civic training
- Infill and reinvestment, not urban sprawl—well-planned growth, management of sprawl, and development in the city's core rather than on the periphery
- Abundant urban green space and recreation areas—recreation and green space within the city, including neighborhood and regional parks, common space, community gardens, bike and walking paths, linear and river parks, trees, and urban landscaping
- Protected natural desert environment—the protection of the Sonoran Desert ecosystem and protection of washes, hillsides, open space, and wildlife
- Better-paying jobs—the wages, job quality, job diversity, and an improved standard of living
- Clean air and quality water—the reduced pollution and provision of clean, potable water
- People-oriented neighborhoods—the designing new neighborhoods and investing in old neighborhoods to promote a mix of commercial and residential uses, a pedestrian focus, landscaping and aesthetics, and interaction among residents
- Respected historic and cultural resources—the preservation and celebration of local landmarks, buildings, neighborhoods, archeological treasures, open spaces, cultures, and traditions that make Tucson unique
- Quality job training—the education, training, and skill development that lead to high-quality, living wage jobs
- Reduced poverty and greater equality of opportunity—the fair distribution of resources and creation of opportunities to overcome poverty and social and economic inequality

- Strong local businesses—the local economy, particularly small, Tucson-based businesses
- Efficient use of natural resources—the conservation of resources and use of sustainable energy sources
- Successful downtown—the cultural and commercial aspects of the city center

Strategic Plan

Livable Tucson is no longer an active program in its original form. It has evolved into a city strategic plan that focuses more narrowly on six priorities: transportation, growth, neighborhoods, good government, downtown, and economic development. Thus, the plan is more specific than Livable Tucson in that it identifies projects and programs that the city is undertaking to accomplish those priorities. In this way, the plan is tied to the budget; it has specific dollars associated with it and, therefore, is more likely to produce results. The six areas also focus on what the city of Tucson is responsible for and can control.

The focus shifted because the original goals were too complex and broad. The goals were not tied to the city budget, meaning that public dollars were not directly aimed at trying to achieve the goals. Also, many goals were actually the responsibility of other jurisdictions such as school districts or the county. It was difficult for the city to influence the other jurisdictions. Furthermore, turnover among leadership proved to be another obstacle (there is now a new city council and city manager). The new leadership had different ideas about how they wanted to move forward. This change doesn't mean the 17 key goals have been abandoned. Instead, the goals of the Livable Tucson program were incorporated into the city's general plan in the 2001 update approved by voters.

Source:
Excerpted and adapted with permission from City of Tucson 2000 (E).

Visioning—Steps 1 and 2

How do you *want* your area to look in 20 years? Follow the instructions below to create your group's vision for the future.

The Oregon Model

Step 1 Where are we now?	Step 2 Where are we going?	Step 3 Where do we want to be?	Step 4 How do we get there?
COMMUNITY PROFILE	**TREND STATEMENT**	**VISION STATEMENT**	**ACTION PLAN**
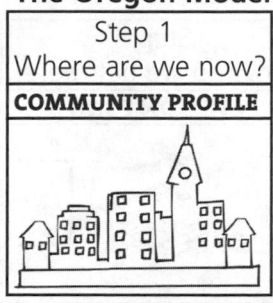	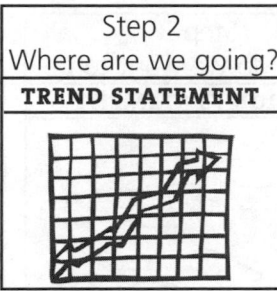	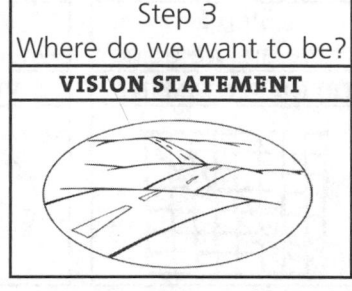	

Step 1: Where are we now? Community Profile

1. On a large piece of paper, draw a current map of the area, including as many important details as you can. Details should reflect what qualities of your community you deem important.

2. Learn more! What approaches will your group use to discover more about the area's characteristics?

3. Conduct research. What were the results of this research?

4. What do you consider the best features of the area?

5. Which features of the area would you most like to change?

6. Which elements best express the area's character and help define your sense of place?

Step 2: Where are we going? Trend Statement

1. Do you think the area looks different today from how it did 20 years ago? Explain. What is your evidence?

2. What are the current direction and rate of change? What is your evidence? How could you learn more?

3. Do you think the change will be positive or negative? Explain.

4. If change continues in this manner, how do you think the area will be different in 20 years? Explain.

5. On a large piece of paper, draw a map depicting how you imagine the area will look in 20 years. Use the same scale as in step 1. Label your drawing clearly.

Visioning—Steps 3 and 4

How do you *want* your area to look in 20 years? Follow the instructions below to create your group's vision for the future.

The Oregon Model

Step 1 Where are we now?	Step 2 Where are we going?	Step 3 Where do we want to be?	Step 4 How do we get there?
COMMUNITY PROFILE	**TREND STATEMENT**	**VISION STATEMENT**	**ACTION PLAN**
		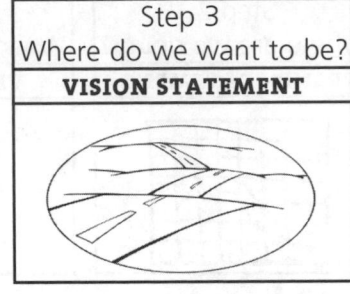	

Step 3: Where do we want to be? Vision Statement

1. Brainstorm and imagine your area in 20 years. Think about all the components that you might want your area to include. Be creative, positive, and constructive! Don't worry about how to make it possible—instead, focus on components you want to include in an ideal world. Think about how to design an area that would promote a good quality of life. Make a list that includes everyone's ideas.

2. Mark your three best ideas.

3. Articulate your ideas in a clear, concise vision statement (no longer than a short paragraph).

4. Draw your idealized vision of the future on a large piece of paper, using the same scale as in steps 1 and 2. Be sure to express your three best ideas clearly, as well as any other components that your group agrees to include. Label your drawing, as appropriate.

Step 4: How do we get there? Action Plan

1. What steps are necessary to implement your vision statement?

2. Who might support the plan? Oppose it?

7

Far-Reaching Decisions

Students develop graphic organizers and creative presentations to illustrate how individual decisions can impact the local environment, as well as distant communities. They also measure their own ecological footprint.

Subjects
Environmental Studies, Geography, Social Studies

Concepts
1.6 Successful technologies are those that are appropriate to the efficient and sustainable use of resources, and to the preservation and enhancement of environmental quality.

2.11 All humans consume products and thereby affect the availability of renewable and nonrenewable natural resources.

5.9 Consumers "drive" the marketplace with their demands for goods and services. Such demands shift with time and may have positive or negative effects on the resource base and environmental quality.

Skills
Analyzing, Classifying and Categorizing, Determining Causes and Effects, Establishing Criteria, Interpreting, Organizing Information, Predicting, Reasoning, Researching

Materials
Copies of student pages, paper, markers. Optional: Internet connection and graphic organizer software

Time Considerations
Part A: Two 50-minute periods

Part B: Two 50-minute periods

Objectives
▶ Students will analyze a case study about the challenges faced by Joshua Tree National Park as a result of the surrounding urban and suburban development.

▶ Students will explore how the choices we make about the foods we eat, the products we purchase, the energy we use, and the communities we develop affect distant communities.

▶ Students will work in teams to develop a presentation highlighting the far-reaching consequences of our actions.

Assessments
▶ Encourage students to write a detailed account from the perspective of a consumer product or a resource, tracing its path and experiences from points A to Z. For instance, students might write a story about a cow that grows up in Brazil and ends up as a hamburger at a fastfood restaurant in their community. Or they might write about a drop of oil trapped underground in Kuwait that ends up powering a car being driven to high school by a student. Stuendts should be sure to address the effects along the way.

▶ Invite students to first write a detailed documentation of the consequences of five of their recent decisions. Then, have students imagine that they changed the five decisions (for better or for worse). How would those changes affect the local and distant communities differently?

Background

The world contains enough to satisfy every man's need, but never enough for our greed.

—Mahatma Gandhi

Think Globally, Act Locally

One of the most popular environmental slogans proclaims, "Think Globally, Act Locally." What does it mean? Rene Dubos, an advisor to the United Nations Conference on the Human Environment, is credited with first using the phrase in 1972. Dubos suggests that ecological consciousness should begin at home.[1] We must consider the ecological, economic, and cultural differences of our local surroundings in order to address global environmental problems. Decades later, the powerful catchphrase is a cornerstone of the environmental movement. It empowers people and suggests that each of us can make a difference. It implies that we don't need to save the world single-handedly, but that if enough of us work locally to make Earth a better place to live, our collective efforts can have global consequences.

The catchphrase also implies that we are all interconnected. The somewhat arbitrary boundaries that divide neighborhoods, counties, states, and even countries generally do not apply to environmental effects. Our local actions may indeed have repercussions felt around the globe. For example, Japan's demand for timber has fueled the harvesting of forests in Southeast Asia.[2] We're even having an effect on areas where the nearest human may be thousands of miles away. For instance, global climate change has been blamed for the melting of sea ice around the Antarctic Peninsula, which, in turn, is the suspected cause of the decline in Adelie penguins that rely on the ice for shelter and survival.[3] Some activities directly affect the food we eat. Pollock, salmon, and other species caught in the Bering Sea off the coast of Alaska make up about half the U.S. fish catch. However, illegal fishing in the Russian waters of the Bering Sea poses a significant threat to the viability of the fisheries.[4]

We all affect our global environment. For example, here in the United States, we emit greenhouse gasses into our shared atmosphere and contribute to global climate change as we drive to the local mall or turn up the heat at home. At the same time, when we plant native trees or plants and help preserve green space in our communities, we contribute to the cleaning of our air and help combat global climate change. Although solving the problem is not this simple, those few examples illustrate that our behaviors influence the world around us.

Thinking beyond our local communities is especially important given the globalization of our economy. Increasingly, the products we buy come from many miles away. Read the small print on the items in your kitchen cabinets and bedroom closet for examples. Today, we're likely to wear a shirt made in the Philippines, relax on a sofa made in Italy, and drink coffee grown in Colombia. We are also more likely to drive a car made in Japan that is fueled by oil from Saudi Arabia.

What about the food you eat? Do you have an international palate? Although we may not consider our food to be ethnic cuisine, many of the raw materials can be traced around the globe. Perhaps you enjoy bananas from Ecuador, tea from India, grapes from Chile, rice from China, or vanilla from Madagascar.

Far, Far Away

We simply cannot grow our way to sustainability in a world that sees people first as potential consumers and only second as responsible citizens.

—Mathis Wackernagel et al. (E)

Although our purchasing decisions and patterns of resource use may feel like very personal choices, they can affect our own communities and distant people, economies, and habitats—for better or for worse. We all make choices every day. For example, how do you decide what to add to your cart as you walk down the grocery store aisles? Most of us base our choices on cost, brand, nutrition, quality, or convenience. Some people, generally those with the luxury of choice, also consider the environmental effects associated with their options—perhaps selecting organic items to encourage the use of pesticide-free farming methods and to promote healthy soil, water, and wildlife habitat. Other shoppers might select locally grown items to minimize the environmental costs associated with transportation and to support local farmers.

The consumer wields surprisingly strong power. For instance, when we buy recycled products, organic foods, and fuel-efficient cars, we support the communities that produce the products, and we help create a future market. When we purchase disposable products, inefficient appliances and cars, and highly processed foods, though, we send a different message to companies and communities.

Ecological Footprint

What is your ***ecological footprint***? In other words, how are you impacting the Earth by the choices you make in consuming particular products and services. The ecological footprint measures how much land and water we need to produce the resources we consume and to absorb the waste we make.[5]

Each action an individual makes has an impact on the planet's ecosystem. How much can the Earth's resources provide and for how many? Can the Earth's biological capacity be sustained at the current level?

The ecological footprint attempts to measure that impact. There have been different proposed models to measure and analyze humanity's ecolgcal footprint. One group, the Global Footprint Network, estimates that today the ecological footprint is 23% larger than the planet can regenerate. That would mean that it would take one year and two months for the Earth to regenerate what the population of the world use in a single year.[6] Other ecological footprint scales use the measurement of how many Earth's it would take to sustain the current rate of consumption to insure that future generations are at least as well off as we are now.

Furthermore, we need to save space and resources for the other species that share our planet. In the words of noted conservationist George Schaller, "We cannot afford another century like this one [i.e., the 20th century]."[7] According to renowned biologist Peter Raven, the current extinction rate is now approaching 1,000 times the background (preindustrial) rate. If current trends continue, between one-third and two-thirds of all plant and animal species are predicted to be lost, mainly in the tropics, during the second half of the 21st century.[8]

Invisible Impact

Can you see your effect on the Earth? People living in small villages, especially in the developing world, tend to observe the consequences of their behaviors. If the water supply is polluted, villagers may fall sick. If the trees

are cut down, the soil may wash away or the village may flood. If the fish supply is depleted, protein sources might become scarce. If the forest is well managed, resources abound.

Most of us in the United States don't live in small villages where we see the effects of our daily behaviors. We don't envision the coffee beans traveling thousands of miles by donkey cart, trucks, and planes to arrive at our local grocery store—or the resulting pollution. Furthermore, we don't see the potential impact in local streams after we overfertilize our lawns. And when we bask in a hot shower, we don't necessarily think of our possible contribution to air pollution and aquifer depletion. The truth is, we do need resources to live our lives. But, we also have choices. In many instances, a little awareness can help inform our decisions. A real challenge to the environmental movement is helping people see the consequences of their decisions.

As Michael Hough (1995) writes in *Cities and Natural Processes*,

"Much of our daily existence is spent in surroundings designed to conceal the processes that sustain life…. The curb and catchbasin that make rainwater disappear without [a] trace below ground, cut the visible links between the natural water cycles, the storm sewers that dispose of it into streams and the lakes and the rivers that ultimately receive it. We are unaware of the ecological degradation that occurs to aquatic life and to the beaches that have to be closed after a heavy rain."

Generally speaking, our current economic system treats environmental degradation as an externality; environmental costs are not factored into the price a consumer pays for a product or service.[9] For example, the environmental costs associated with the disposal of cars do not appear in the customer price. The cost is sometimes passed on to the taxpayer and is always exacted from the planet and its biota.

Role of Technology

As the number of people living on Earth grows, we reach for new resources around the globe. Technology has facilitated our ability to extract and process resources from the farthest corners of remote habitats, whether we're searching for oil in the Arctic National Wildlife Refuge, harvesting fish from deep Antarctic waters, or mining for gold in the mountains of Indonesia. In some cases, the resources we extract are exported thousands of miles away. For instance, trees harvested from the Congo might end up as coffee tables in French homes. The profits generated from the initial resource harvest may or may not filter back into local economies and local families.

Technology also facilitates our movement into previously uninhabitable or undesirable regions, extending our presence into habitats previously reserved for other wild species. In the United States, we transform parched deserts into watered towns, build condos on filled wetlands, and level hills to expand our cities. Undoubtedly, humans are resourceful and industrious. We are also increasingly recognizing that our actions do have repercussions that affect the planet.

Our current challenge lies in better understanding the Earth's systems so we can better predict the consequences of our actions and minimize undesirable outcomes—locally, regionally, and internationally. Furthermore, just as technology can have negative effects, so too can it be used to benefit the Earth. Technology is responsible for the new methods to clean up oil spills, the harnessing of solar energy, and the innovative redesign of fishing nets to reduce unintended dolphin and turtle take.

Innovative Steps

Innovative steps to help reduce our effects on the planet offer promise for the future. For example, cities such as Seattle, Washington, and San Jose, California, give residents an incentive to reduce their household waste by charging for collecting according to the volume generated.[10] In Florida, Manatee and Sarasota Counties have found creative new ways to preserve scarce groundwater resources, reduce pollutants discharged into the Sarasota Bay, and use treated wastewater to grow produce and citrus.[11] China, the world's largest user of coal—a major source of air pollution and of greenhouse gasses—has recently begun to cut its consumption despite continued fast economic growth. China is switching to natural gas, cutting coal subsidies, and investing heavily in improved energy efficiency. In fact, China has shut down 60,000 smoky and inefficient industrial boilers and improved its energy efficiency by 47 percent since the early 1980s.[12] Our future effect on the planet will depend, in part, on whether or not we can find ways to minimize our negative repercussions and promote ecological health.

Through the following activity, students will realize that their purchases and daily decisions can affect both natural resource policy and the economies of distant communities. They will also come to understand that their power as consumers in the global economy means their choices have environmental repercussions, both positive and negative, beyond the local community.

Endnotes

1   Eblen and Eblen 1994 (A).
2   Harrison and Pearce 2000 (E).
3   Greenpeace 1994 (E).
4   Burns 2003 (E).
5   Earthdaynetwork/Redefining Progress 2004 (E).
6   Global Footprint Network 2005 (E)
7   Harrison and Pearce 2000 (E).
8   Australian Broadcasting Corporation 2000 (E).
9   Santoriello and Block 1996 (E).
10 Beatley and Manning 1997 (A).
11 Friedman 1996 (E).
12 Harrison and Pearce 2000 (E).

Letters following author and date citations refer to sections in the bibliography (Appendix B) where the reader can find full data about the sources cited.

- Copy the "Case Study: Joshua Tree National Park" student pages for each student.
- Copy the "Decision-Making Topics" student pages so that each student on each team has the pages with his or her team's topic.
- Review Appendix F "Teaching Controversial issues" to gain some ideas on facilitating discussions and preparing for the activitiy.

Doing the Activity

Part A

1. Ask the class, "What decisions have you made today?" Solicit a few responses (examples might include what to wear, what to eat, or how to get to school). Categorize those responses (e.g., transportation, food choice, shopping).

2. Have each student draw a diagram illustrating the connections between a decision they made over the past 24 hours and everyone and everything that might have been affected by it. The diagram should indicate the nature of each consequence. See the following samples (Figures 7.1 and 7.2).

Note: Consider using graphic organizer software to help the students diagram the consequences. For example, the Inspiration® software program offers a powerful visual learning tool that enables students to develop ideas and organize thinking. Its integrated diagramming and outlining environments work together to help students comprehend concepts and information. To learn more or for a free trial, check out www.inspiration.com. Other useful software programs are SmartDraw (www.smartdraw.com) and Mindjet's MindManager (www.mindjet.com).

3. Invite several students to share their diagrams. Discuss the extent of the consequences, and ask the following questions: How far away were the consequences felt? How many people were affected? What was the nature of the connections (e.g., economic, emotional, physical, environmental)? Can anyone else think of other possible repercussions? Did students list any positive

Figure 7.1. Consequences of the Decision to Drive to School

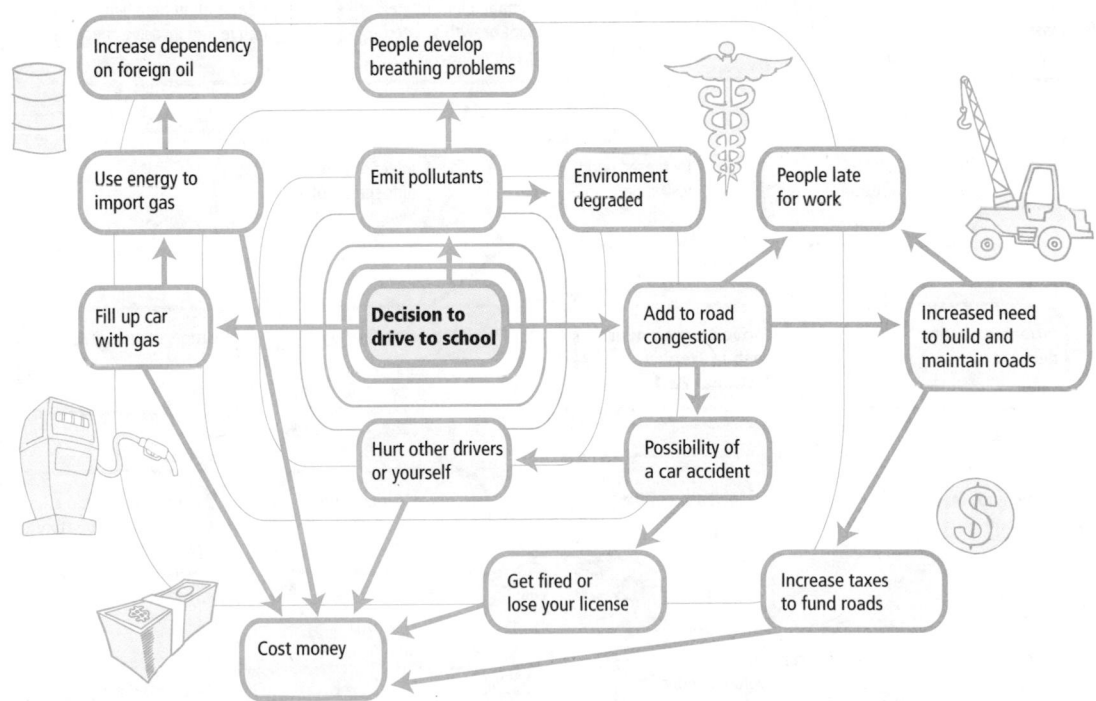

impacts – instances that might improve conditions for the park? Did the decision-maker consider any or all of those effects when making the decision? Would doing so have made a difference? Make sure students update their diagram with any additional connections from the discussion.

4. Distribute copies of the case study "Joshua Tree National Park." Working in teams, students will read the case study and diagram the effect on the park. You may reference examples from the diagram illustrated in Figure 7.2 to get them started.

5. Next, invite the teams to develop solutions for reducing the negative effects on the park. The teams should also detail how the suggested solutions might affect others. Would the idea be accepted? Why or why not? Who would the decision favor? What is a fair solution? Who should have the power to make decisions about issues with far-reaching consequences?

6. Invite each team to share its diagrams and solutions. Compare and contrast the teams' ideas.

Part B

7. Encourage students to calculate their ecological footprints. Check out www.earthday.org. Scroll down the page and select the tab marked "footprint". How do students' footprints compare to the average American's footprint?

8. Divide the class into teams of three or four students (either the same teams or new teams). Give the members of each team a copy of their assigned "Decision Making Topic."

Figure 7.2. Consequences of the Decision to Move Near Joshua Tree National Park

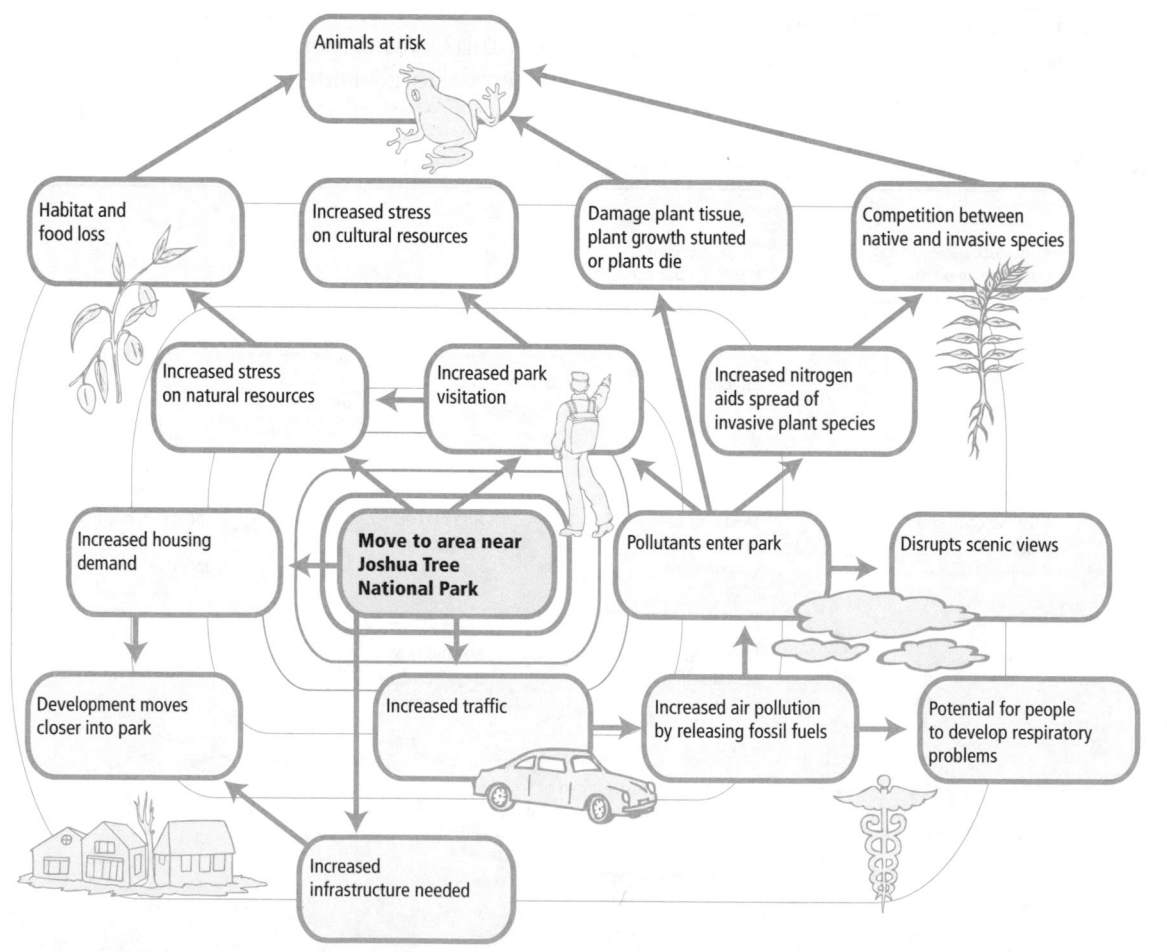

9. Instruct the teams to read about their topic and to discuss the issue, using the questions at the end as a guide. Each team should assign a note-taker to record key points made by all team members and a mediator to ensure that all voices are heard and that no one dominates. Mention that the notes will be collected at the end of class and assessed for thoughtful participation by all members. The purpose of the discussion is for each person to share, explore, and clarify his or her own thoughts, not to convince others of any one opinion.

10. After 15 minutes of group discussion, consider having students stop and write independently for 10 minutes on the topic. Instruct them to use the questions in their discussion topics as writing prompts.

11. Explain that each team will be responsible for developing a 10-minute presentation about its topic. The goal of the presentation is to convey the team members' ideas about how an individual's actions can affect distant communities.

12. Share the following assessment criteria with the teams so they can prepare their presentations appropriately. Encourage students to contribute their ideas to the assessment criteria.
- Depth of understanding: Displayed thorough understanding of the issue and demonstrated how individual actions may affect others
- Research: Gathered outside information to strengthen their argument
- Presentation: Delivered a smooth presentation based on careful preparation
- Convincing argument: Clearly expressed personal conviction; showed that team members were invested

13. Have each student conduct independent research to strengthen the presentation. Assign as homework or as class work for the following day.

14. Instruct each team to decide what the format will be for its presentation and how best to express the different perspectives of the team members. Possible formats are a debate, a skit,

a set of two-minute speeches conveying different views, a news brief, or a set of interviews. Students might also develop "reverse ads" that highlight the negative impacts of a product (e.g., a manufactured good such as a car, a food item, or an energy source) instead of the benefits to the consumer.

15. Invite the teams to deliver their presentations to the class.

16. Use the following questions to lead a final discussion:
- What do the four different topics have in common? How do they differ?
- Do you think an individual's decisions are significant at a larger scale? How? When? Always?
- Do the team presentations and ideas shed any new light on the Joshua Tree case study?
- Do any of the topics inspire citizen action? If yes, what do you propose?
- Can you think of any other topics that you could have researched to understand how personal choices have far-reaching repercussions?

17. If time permits, use students' ideas about action steps to develop an action project. See the Project Learning Tree's GreenWorks! Guide for resources: www.plt.org.

Enrichment

- Encourage students to research a local issue that crosses community boundaries. Who are the parties involved? What is the source of the problem? What are possible steps for resolution? Students can compare their issue to the Joshua Tree case study.

- Take this one step further, and have students investigate food, shopping, and energy use in their own community and then report back to class. They should include how decisions in their community affect other communities in the United States and abroad.

Case Study: Joshua Tree National Park

The Los Angeles metropolitan area in southern California has seen tremendous population growth since the early 1900s (see Table 1). The 2000 Census named Los Angeles County the most populated county in the United States. The growth has continued to spill into the surrounding counties, three of which (Orange, San Bernardino, and Riverside) are also among the 20 most populated counties in the United States. Population growth on such a large scale presents huge challenges, including pressures on public services, sprawling suburbs, and the resulting environmental and social problems. For example, in 2002, the American Lung Association named the Los Angeles–Riverside–Orange County region as the metropolitan area with the worst ozone air pollution. In that same year, San Bernardino County was named the county with the worst ozone air pollution. Those two areas have filled the number-one slot on both lists since the American Lung Association first began publishing reports on air quality several years ago.

Table 1. Los Angeles County Population and Population Density: 1900–2000

Year	Population	Population Density (residents/mi²)
1900	170,298	42
1950	4,151,687	1,023
2000	9,519,338	2,345

Source: U.S. Census Bureau, www.census.gov.

A World Apart

Travel 140 miles east of Los Angeles into San Bernardino and Riverside Counties, and you will find yourself in a different world, amid evergreen creosote bushes and cacti, jackrabbits and lizards, and some of the best rock climbing in the world. Welcome to Joshua Tree National Park (JTNP), home to several of California's ecoregions, including two desert ecosystems that come together in a dramatic and unique transition zone within the park. Those desert ecosystems owe their distinguishing characteristics to differences in elevation. The dry Colorado Desert lies below 3,000 feet in elevation in the eastern region of the park. Evergreen creosote bushes, funnel-shaped ocotillo with canelike branches, and fluffy-looking yet very spiny teddy bear cholla characterize the area. Climb to higher elevations of 3,000 feet or more in the northern region of the park, and you enter the wetter and somewhat cooler Mojave Desert. This is the only place you will find the unique plant, the Joshua tree, that gives the national park its name and its shaggy branches and spiky leaves.

The park is not all desert. Various mountain ranges border the park, and several can even be found within the park where elevations reach more than 5,000 feet. Scattered throughout the park are numerous natural springs and seeps, both important water sources for wildlife. There are also five natural oases, islands of green vegetation that owe their existence to the small amount of water close enough to the surface to support life. Those oases provide habitat for the California fan palm, the largest native palm in the United States and the only native palm in the western United States.

Case Study: Joshua Tree National Park (cont.)

Desert Alive

JTNP is home to a rich variety of wildlife. The desert may not seem a likely spot for amphibians, which need water in their aquatic stage, but, nonetheless, you can find the California tree frog (a species of special concern) and two types of toads. You can also see lizards basking in the sun, and you might even run into snakes in the area where six species of rattlesnake live. You might sneak a peek at the state reptile, the elusive and threatened desert tortoise, which spends 95 percent of its time under the ground. More than 250 bird species have been identified, including the golden eagle and the roadrunner. As part of the Pacific flyway, many migratory birds travel through JTNP as they abandon the heavy snows of nearby mountains, seeking warmer weather. Fifty-two species of mammals live within the park, including 24 small rodent species and 21 bat species. Nocturnal prowlers include bighorn sheep, black-tailed jackrabbits, bobcats, coyotes, foxes, and mule deer.

In 1936, the area was designated as a National Monument to protect the region's plant and animal diversity and the cultural resources of early people (humans have inhabited the area of the park for more than 9,000 years!). In 1994, President Bill Clinton signed the California Desert Protection Act, designating Joshua Tree National Monument as a national park and adding more than 230,000 acres to the protected area. Today, more than 1,250,000 people visit JTNP annually. They come to enjoy the unique scenery and educational programs, bicycle, bird watch, camp, draw, hike, paint, picnic, and rock climb. Many people come for the quiet and solitude that only a desert can provide.

Something in the Air

Although the biodiversity and topographic diversity of JTNP distinguish it from the neighboring urban regions, air pollution is a problem that both areas share. Years ago, you could stand at Key's View, look out at the desert, and see across the Salton Sea to Mount Signal in Mexico, some 100 miles away. Yet today, on the warm winter days and during the hot summer months, visitors arriving at that same spot are lucky to see Mount San Jacinto just across the Coachella Valley—about 20 miles away. Interfering with the view is a haze of photochemical (light-reacting) smog. Ozone (O_3) is a light reacting or photochemical smog that produces a brown haze in the troposphere, the Earth's lower atmosphere. Another type of smog that interferes with the views of Joshua Tree National Park is from very fine particulate matter (e.g. dust and aerosols). The combination of the two types of smog place JTNP at the top of another notorious list: national parks with the worst air quality.

Much of the smog originates in the Los Angeles metropolitan area and surrounding counties. Each day of intense heat and sunlight in the Los Angeles Basin, ozone is formed when airborne gasoline fumes and industrial solvents combine with nitrogen oxides from vehicles and fossil fuel burning power plants. Wind blows the jumble of pollutants east, away from Los Angeles. As the sunlight and temperature increase during the day, the mass of pollutants warms and rises up and over the Little San Bernardino Mountains. As night arrives and temperatures drop, the mass begins to cool and settles in the valleys of JTNP, creating a layer of polluted air that covers much of the park. The same process occurs day after day. Increased sunlight and high temperatures lead to even higher concentrations of harmful ozone.

Summer months see the most days with the poorest air quality, but recently, the number of poor air quality days in the winter has been increasing. A combination of geography and climate make JTNP a prime location for the smog accumulation that decreases visibility. Other consequences of the increased levels of ozone in the troposphere include:

Case Study: Joshua Tree National Park (cont.)

- Increased nitrogen deposition that is believed to aid the spread of invasive plants
- Damage to plant tissue causing diminished growth and sometimes plant mortality
- Human health problems such as irritation and damage of the respiratory system and aggravation of asthma

Under Pressure

JTNP also faces challenges from growth and development in communities adjacent to the park. People are flocking to the area because of its lower cost of living (compared to Los Angeles), to escape the problems of city life, such as crime and traffic, or simply to reconnect with nature. The surrounding communities south of the park include resort towns like Palm Springs, Indian Wells, LaQuinta, and Palm Desert. North of the park lie the towns of Twenty-nine Palms and Yucca Valley, the U.S. Marine Corps Air Ground Combat Center (the largest U.S. Marine Corps base in the world), and Joshua Tree (an unincorporated rural community that has grown around the needs of tourists visiting JTNP). Population growth is affecting all of those areas, and the subsequent development is encroaching on the park.

A 9,000-acre area of land directly south of the park has been proposed as a site for the Joshua Hills development. Plans include 7,000 housing units, a three-million-square-foot industrial park, 12 golf courses, three hotels, a convention center, and several shopping centers. In addition, the lands surrounding the park are prime targets for power plants as California scrambles to meet the growing demand for electricity. One power plant has already been built near the park borders, and numerous others have been proposed. As more people move into areas around the park, they require new infrastructure and generate additional pollutants. The smog problem is exacerbated, and park visibility is further reduced.

Those problems are not the only consequences of increased population and development in the counties surrounding the park. Nineteen million people live within a three-hour drive of the park, and adding more people means increasing demands on the local infrastructure. Desert groundwater supplies are being depleted to meet increased water needs. The sanitation districts of Los Angeles County have proposed placing a landfill (the largest in the United States) next to JTNP. The National Parks Conservation Association has filed lawsuits against the proposed landfill, believing such a landfill would threaten air and water quality, create loose trash that would blow into the park, and destroy the views and solitude enjoyed by park visitors. More people in the area would also mean more visitors to the park. Having so many people enjoy the park has a downside—a decrease in the opportunities for solitude, one of the main draws of JTNP. Higher usage often translates into more stress on the fragile ecosystem. Higher usage also increases wear and tear on the cultural resources—such as rock art, historic buildings, and archeological sites—that are already threatened by environmental pressures from the additional sprawl and population.

Steps for the Future

Within the park, staff members are doing what they can to decrease their own environmental impacts. They are increasing their use of solar energy at campgrounds and park buildings. Soon all park vehicles will run on compressed natural gas or another alternative fuel. Yet, protecting JTNP from further harm will also require the efforts and actions of the individuals and communities that surround the park (whether they are adjacent or 140 miles away). Perhaps JTNP Superintendent Ernie Quintana put it best:

"We're at a critical crossroads now. In the past 10 years, Joshua Tree National Park has come of age. The pressures are from increasing visitation and [from] increasing by urban encroachment....

Case Study: Joshua Tree National Park (cont.)

We, all municipalities and regulatory agencies, need to take a look now and project into the future on how to protect and provide open space, recreation, and development opportunities. We have to be wise where we want development to occur and protect areas of open space. Through planning, we have to do a better job of protecting the park and the quality of life we came here for—the openness, the night skies. If we're not careful, we'll lose it all."

Besides their work inside the park, JTNP staff members are also working with the surrounding communities. They conduct education programs to help communities see and appreciate the value of their park neighbor. Park staff members have set up a web-cam so anyone with an Internet connection can monitor the changes in air quality at specific points in the park. Such efforts are meant to encourage members of the surrounding communities to be "advocates" for the park and to realize that they can take important steps (even if they live 140 miles away in Los Angeles) to help protect the park from further environmental damage.

Questions to Consider:

- Do you think citizens in Los Angeles realize that their actions affect desert plants, animals, ecosystems, and people over a hundred miles away?
- What other steps do you think should be taken?
- How is the air quality in your town? (Visit www.epa.gov or contact local air quality management district.)
- Do you know of any similar situations near you?
- How do you think the actions of citizens in your community might affect distant communities and ecosystems?
- Are there negative impacts besides air quality and water pollution from your community that may be harming wildlife that is either migrating through or living at a distance?

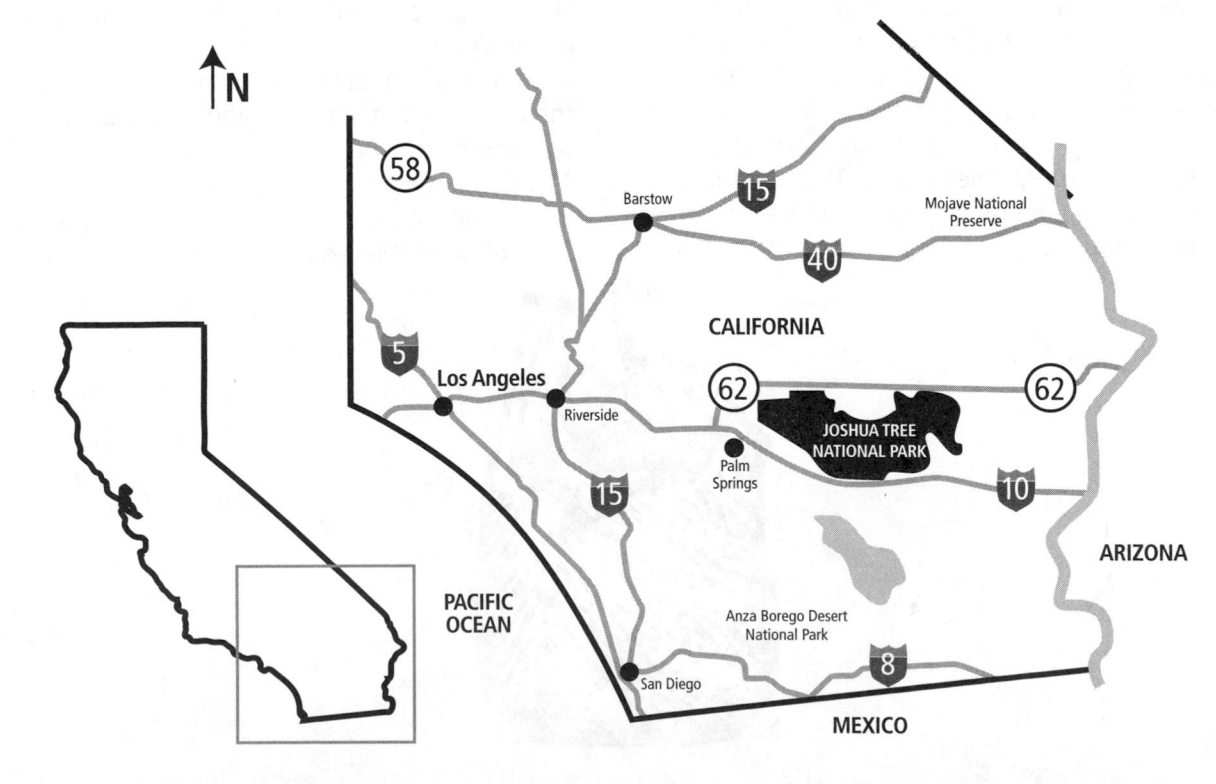

Decision-Making Topics

Food Choices

Walk into most grocery stores in the United States today, and you'll find a world of choices before you: full fat, low fat, no fat; low sodium; bulk or single servings; fresh or frozen; raw or processed; organic; vegetarian or vegan; low cholesterol; locally grown or imported; generic or name brand; packaged or loose; with or without preservatives; with or without artificial flavors and colors; recycled or recyclable; and so forth. The choices can be overwhelming. How do we decide?

The decisions we make affect not only our families but also the companies that produce the products, the communities that depend on the companies for jobs, and the communities that are affected by the manufacturing processes. For example, if we buy bananas from Costa Rica, we support that country's economy and help provide local jobs. If we buy organic apples, we send the message that we prefer products grown without synthetic chemicals, and we help promote healthy habitats for wildlife at the same time. If we buy fruits and vegetables out of season, we contribute to air pollution by encouraging the transport of goods from many miles away. And if we buy local produce, we benefit local families and the environment.

What Do You Think?

- How do you decide what to eat?
- What choices do you have in the foods you eat?
- Who buys most of the food you eat? What criteria are considered in the purchasing decisions?
- What factors do you think are most important?
- Read the labels on foods your family has recently purchased. What do the labels tell you? What don't they tell you?
- How do our decisions affect the environment?
- Are environmental costs figured into food prices? How? Should they be?
- How do you think our food purchasing decisions have changed over the past 50 years? Can you name 10 items that would not have been found in a grocery store 50 years ago?
- How important is health? Do you think Americans today are more or less healthy than 50 years ago? Explain.
- How do you think our food choices in the United States differ from choices in other nations?
- Would you be willing to pay more to protect the environment through your purchases? If so, how much more? 1 percent? 10 percent? 100 percent?
- How could you learn more about the repercussions of your choices on distant communities?

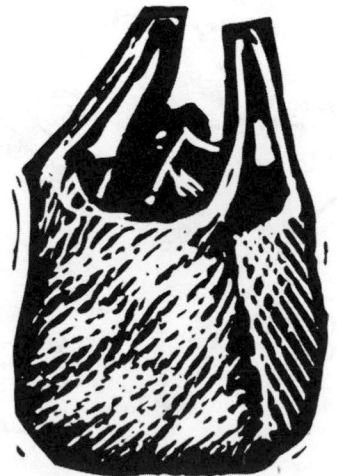

Decision-Making Topics (cont.)

Consumer Choices

Consumers have great power. The decisions we make as consumers send messages to companies and influence their future behavior. For example, when we buy recycled paper, we support companies that provide environmentally conscious products. When we buy high-quality reusable products instead of single-use disposable items, we send the message that we are not going to contribute our dollars to a throwaway society.

Our purchasing decisions can also influence the lives of people, plants, and animals many miles away because what we buy affects how the Earth is treated. For example, if we choose disposable items, we use additional natural resources and energy as we add to the mountains of trash at local or distant landfills. If we purchase clothes made of organically grown cotton and colored with natural dyes, we help reduce water pollution and promote healthier soils. If we buy things like acid-washed jeans, however, we contribute to water pollution and groundwater depletion.

And sometimes the products we purchase have a more direct effect on the communities that provide them. For example, by purchasing products that use harmful chemicals, such as some pesticides, we may affect the health of crop workers. Or, if we buy products manufactured by companies with poor human-rights records, we may inadvertently support the companies' behavior. But when we buy products produced in our own community, we are supporting our local economy.

In some cases, purchases can offer win–win solutions. If we buy fuel-efficient cars, for instance, we encourage companies to develop more efficient models, we reduce our contribution to air pollution, and we help slow global warming.

What Do You Think?

- How can our shopping decisions affect the global environment?
- How can our shopping decisions affect people in distant communities?
- Are environmental costs figured into the price of our products? How? Should they be?
- How do we feel the effects of environmental problems in other countries?
- What do you support when you purchase from megastores? What do you support by purchasing from local stores? What are the pros and cons of each?
- Look at the labels on your clothes. Where were the clothes manufactured?
- Do you shop on the Internet? What are the economic, environmental, and social consequences?
- Explore the Natural Abode website (www.thenaturalabode.com). What do you discover about their products? What factors would influence whether you purchased their products?
- Do you think consumers should be free to decide the future through their purchasing decisions, or do you believe government policies should be put in place? (For example, the Convention on International Trade in Endangered Species (CITES) is a wildlife treaty signed by more than 150 countries to regulate imports and exports of wild animals and plants that are threatened by trade.)
- Would you be willing to pay more to protect the environment through your purchases? If so, how much more? 1 percent? 10 percent? 100 percent?

Decision-Making Topics (cont.)

Community Planning

Growth places incredible pressures on communities. Many U.S. areas are under development pressure that places greater demands on already stressed natural resources. Communities struggle to meet the needs of their residents as the population increases and as people seek or require more and larger homes, schools, roads, and recreation areas. It can be a challenge to find space for people to live and work while still preserving open space and keeping ecosystems intact. How can towns and cities manage the social, environmental, and economic demands that result from growth? Communities pursue different strategies, including the following:

• Create housing of varied costs and sizes.
• Write zoning laws that allow for mixed-use development.
• Provide mass transportation.
• Offer opportunities for local employment.
• Supply within-community sewer treatment.
• Locate schools within walking distance of homes.
• Retain or create green infrastructure.
• Create shared parking areas.
• Ensure walking or biking access, or both.

Some people dislike the artificiality of planned communities. Others consider them the best solution to reduce sprawl, contain development, promote a community feeling, reduce commuting, trim carbon emissions, create diverse neighborhoods, and provide affordable housing.

What Do You Think?

• Can communities accommodate a growing population *and* preserve their natural resources? Explain.
• Does your community incorporate any of the strategies listed above?
• Do you use mass transit? Do you travel by car? Do you travel by skateboard, ride your bike, or walk? Which do you use more? Why?
• How much of your free time do you spend outdoors? Indoors? Where do you go to socialize? How do you get there? Why do you choose this mode?
• Where do you go for entertainment? How do you get there?
• Where do you go to shop?
• How do you think your personal preferences affect the environment? Locally? Regionally? Beyond?
• How does the design of your community affect other communities in your region?
• How does the design of your community affect wildlife and other natural resources in your community? Your region?
• How do other communities affect your community?
• How could your community be improved to lessen its environmental effects?
• What are your community's greatest strengths? Weaknesses?

Decision-Making Topics (cont.)

Energy Choices

How much energy do you use? Thirty-six percent of the energy consumed in the United States is used residentially to cool and heat homes, to provide lighting, and to run appliances. The energy comes from a variety of sources—largely oil, natural gas, and coal. See Table 2. Investigate data for today. Have the sources of energy for the United States changed since 1998? Why or why not? Will they change in the next 20 years?

Table 2. 1998 Energy Consumption in the United States

Source	Percentage of Total Consumption
Oil	38.8
Natural Gas	23.2
Coal	22.9
Nuclear	7.6
Hydroelectric	3.8
Geothermal	0.3
Biomass	3.2
Solar	0.07
Wind	0.04

Source: http://energy.usgs.gov

What Do You Think?

- Consider all the different ways you have used energy today. How did you get to school? What powers the lights in your classroom?
- Do you have an electrical power plant in your community?
- Where is the nearest electrical power plant?
- What is the source of energy that is used to generate the electricity?
- What are the pros and cons (economic, environmental, social) of the source of energy used in your community?
- Does a better alternative source exist for the energy for your community?

- Do you take any actions to conserve energy? If so, what?
- How do your energy choices affect your local community? The global community?
- Why do you think the United States is the largest energy consumer in the world and also has one of the largest per capita consumption rates of energy? What are some of the ways that people in the United States can reduce their energy consumption? How would this affect total energy consumption in the United States?
- India has one of the smallest rates of energy consumption per capita. What would be the economic, environmental, and social effects if all the people in India were to consume energy at a rate equivalent to that in the United States? See Tables 3 and 4.

Table 3. Oil Consumption in Developed and Developing Countries

Country	Kg oil used per capita per year
Developed country average	4,505
Developing country average	803
United States	7,956
India	477

Source: World Resources Institute 2003 (E).

Table 4. Population of the United States and India as of 2004

Country	Population
United States	294,000,000
India	1,087,000,000

Source: Population Reference Bureau 2004 (E)

Notes

_____

_____

_____

_____

_____

_____

_____

_____

_____

_____

_____

_____

_____

_____

_____

_____

Regional Community Issues: The Ogallala Aquifer

Students investigate a regional issue as they adopt the roles of shareholders and debate solutions to the depletion of North America's largest aquifer.

Subjects
Biology, Environmental Science, Social Studies

Concepts
2.6 International cooperation directed toward conserving resources and protecting environmental quality is beneficial to human health and the well-being of other life forms.

2.7 By reducing waste and recycling materials, individuals and societies can extend the value and utility of resources and also promote environmental quality.

2.9 The quantity and quality of resources and their use—or misuse—by humans affect the standard of living of societies.

3.11 Effective citizen involvement in the environmental decision-making process involves a careful study of all sides of the issues, along with the ability to differentiate between honest, factually accurate information and propaganda.

Skills
Concluding, Decision Making, Defining Problems, Discussing, Identifying Main Ideas, Problem Solving, Researching, Synthesizing and Creating

Materials
Copies of student pages

Time Considerations
Three to four 50-minute periods

Objectives
▶ Students will adopt different shareholder's perspectives as they role-play a regional issue.

▶ Students will understand the interrelationships between local communities in a region.

▶ Students will work in teams to develop an action plan to combat the depletion of a shared natural resource—the Ogallala Aquifer.

Assessments
▶ The "Shareholder's View" student page provides a built-in assessment tool. To add to the activity, ask students to complete a "Shareholder's View" page for other characters on their team.

▶ Instruct students to write a page from the perspective of their assigned stakeholder and to address their thoughts about the team's final action plan. What do they like and dislike about the resolution? How will it affect their life, opportunities, and sense of place?

▶ Following the model of the "Role Cards" provided, have students write a new role card that is based on their perspective as a consumer or citizen who is distant from the Ogallala Aquifer (or someone local if you live in the Great Plains).

▶ The Colorado River is a vital resource for multiple states. Arizona, California, Colorado, New Mexico, Nevada, Utah, and Wyoming all stake a claim to the river. The increasing demands of rapid growth and droughts have heightened the gravity of this water dispute in the West. Have students research the issue to identify various shareholders and their positions.

▶ Water distribution is a critical issue all over the world. Have students research and report on another country or region that is facing water rights issues. Examples of regions to investigate include the following:

▶ Chao Phraya River basin, Thailand

▶ Greater Tokyo region, Japan

▶ Lake Peipsi/Chudskoe Ozero, Estonia and Russia

▶ Lake Titicaca basin, Bolivia and Peru

▶ Ruhuna basin, Sri Lanka

▶ Seine-Normandy basin around Paris, France

▶ Senegal River basin, Guinea, Mali, Mauritania, and Senegal

Background

From babbling streams to raging oceans, water is one of the most common substances on Earth, but in some places it is becoming priceless.

—Roland Wall (E)

What do we need to survive? The quality and quantity of natural resources, such as water, soil, air, and biota, are vital to communities worldwide. The stability and condition of those resources determine the stability and condition of the community in which they are found. It is difficult for a community to thrive and prosper when such resources are degraded and depleted. Yet when resources abound, the community flourishes. As members of a community, our individual uses of natural assets influence our community's management of resources.

How we manage our local resources also determines the effect we have on other communities in different regions, or even countries. For instance, air pollution from the Midwest drifts into northern New York and Canada, where it contributes to acid rain, affects the maple sugar industry, and reduces the diversity and abundance of local fish. In Asia, deforestation in the mountains of Nepal has been blamed for increased flooding in Bangladesh. By learning how to reduce our stresses on natural resources and how to promote healthy communities through informed decision making, we can improve the quality of life for both local and distant communities.

Upstream and Downstream

You've probably heard the slogan "We all live downstream." The ways that our upstream neighbors treat their water resources affects those of us living downstream. Likewise, how we manage our water affects built and natural communities downstream from us, even those hundreds of miles away. In fact, we might also say, "We all live upstream." That perspective places the emphasis on individual responsibility to keep our shared resource flowing and clean so our neighbors downstream can find sustenance from the water. Stewardship of our natural resources promotes healthy ecological systems and processes, benefiting both our neighbors (human and other) and ourselves.

In discussing upstream and downstream issues, we tend to think about moving surface waters such as streams and rivers. But we also share responsibility for other types of common water sources such as wetlands, lakes, oceans, and groundwater. Furthermore, quantity is just as vital as quality in managing our natural inheritance. Does one community have the right to construct a dam that will prevent water from reaching a downstream community? Who owns the water in a river or aquifer? If two drought-stricken towns require more water than is locally available, who has priority in laying claim to a nearby reservoir or aquifer? Who makes the decisions? Politics, power, and economics greatly affect the outcome. In fact, around the world, competition for increasingly

scarce water resources is predicted to be a flashpoint for future conflict. More than 200 river systems cross national boundaries.[1] From the earliest cultures to the present, the ability to harness, control, and maintain water sources has been central to political stability and economic growth. At the same time, losing control of water supplies has been known to lead to panic and social disarray.[2]

Enough for Everyone?

Will we ever run out of water? Or is water an unlimited, renewable resource? We have approximately the same total amount of water today as when our planet was formed. Although water covers approximately 80 percent of Earth's surface, only a 1 percent exists as freshwater available for our use. Although the total amount of water on Earth is finite, it is cycled and recharged constantly through the processes of evaporation, transpiration, and precipitation (the water cycle). Imagine, the water in your glass today may once have quenched the thirst of a dinosaur or watered a prehistoric fern. Yet, we are withdrawing our groundwater faster than we are recharging our groundwater.[3] Another critical concern relating to water use is keeping our freshwater supply clean and healthy. As we increasingly pollute and contaminate our freshwater, we effectively reduce the available supply.

Globally, more than 1 billion people lack access to clean, safe water, and more than three million people die each year from preventable, water-related diseases.[4] Water inequities can be seen throughout the world. Two billion people receive less than the necessary 13 gallons (50 liters) of water required each day for drinking, sanitation, and cooking. In Africa, water withdrawals for household use average 12 gallons (47 liters) per person per day, while in Asia the average is 25 gallons (95 liters). The United States leads the world in water consumption—approximately 153 gallons (578 liters) per person per day, approximately 12 times the average use in Africa.[5]

Over the past 70 years, the global population has tripled and water use has increased sixfold. Experts estimate that at the present per capita rates of consumption, 70 percent of Earth's annual freshwater supply will be used to meet the needs of eight billion people by the year 2025. However, if consumption increases to the level of more developed nations, 90 percent of the annual available supply would be required. In addition to stressing human populations, growing appropriation of freshwater resources for human use reduces the amount available for other species. As we affect riverine, lake, and wetland ecosystems, we affect their plant and animal inhabitants and disrupt the critical natural services that they provide to humans.[6]

Agriculture's Thirst

Worldwide, irrigation and the managed use of water have been essential factors in raising productivity of agriculture and ensuring predictability in outputs. At the close of the 20th century, agriculture accounted for a global average of 70 percent of all water withdrawals, and it is expected to increase approximately 14 percent by 2030.[7] In the United States, irrigation—most of it using grossly inefficient flooding methods—represents 40 percent of direct water consumption.[8]

Alternative methods that improve the efficiency of irrigation offer hope for the future. For example, technologies for measuring soil moisture can help farmers manage water use. Some devices are quite inexpensive, such as gypsum blocks, which measure the soil's electrical conductivity, or tensiometers, which measure the suction of drying soil on a tube of

water. Switching irrigation systems (e.g., using drip irrigation as opposed to sprinklers) can make a significant difference in water use but may be expensive in the short run. Drip irrigation, which waters vegetation at the roots, is by far the most efficient management strategy. It is the least used, however, in part because it is not as effective for some classes of crops, but also because artificially cheap water prices make less-efficient methods less expensive.[9]

In the United States, we are fortunate to have large supplies of freshwater in almost every area of the country. The challenge is to manage this resource in a responsible and practical fashion in order to ensure abundant and high-quality water supplies for future generations.[10]

The Ogallala Aquifer

Although we typically think of lakes and rivers as our sources of freshwater, we actually draw much of our freshwater supply from underground sources. In fact, **groundwater** is the primary source of drinking water for more than half of the people in the United States. Groundwater is found under the ground in layers of sand, gravel, and other unconsolidated material. Those materials have tiny spaces between the small particles that fill with water, accumulating in a large layer called an **aquifer**. Aquifers receive their water when precipitation, such as rain and melted snow, trickle down from the surface to the porous layer. In the United States, we use 90 billion gallons (342 billion liters) of groundwater every day, and more than two-thirds of that is used for irrigation.[11]

Through the following case study about the Ogallala Aquifer in the High Plains, students come to realize that choices made in local communities often affect a much larger area. The Ogallala Aquifer illustrates how remote economic and political decisions can affect a natural resource. The aquifer is huge—it reaches into eight states and holds the record as the largest known groundwater system in North America. Communities across multiple states depend on the groundwater, and entire economies have grown up around this natural resource. Approximately 95 percent of the water pumped from the Ogallala Aquifer irrigates farmers' crops.[12] Consumers across the United States (and abroad) create the demand for products from this region, which include alfalfa, beef, corn, cotton, and wheat, thus sustaining the economy that depends on the aquifer.

Water levels in the aquifer are dropping, more in some places than others. Near Plainview, Texas, water levels dropped from 70 feet in 1956 to 110 feet below the surface in 1974.[13] And the withdrawal rate greatly exceeds the recharge rate of this water supply. What will the future hold? Will we deplete the supply? Who has rights to the water? Which towns and which generations? Will technological innovation reverse this trend? Should we save the aquifer for future water emergencies? Regional decision makers are grappling with those issues. They face the dual challenge of continued growth and economic dependence on the resource. For more information on the Ogallala Aquifer, see the student pages.

In this activity, students will focus on water use in our Great Plains and its ripple effects, thus affecting distant communities and future generations. The Ogallala Aquifer case study offers a great opportunity to explore an authentic, current *"tragedy of the commons."* Focusing on resource distribution helps us become sensitized to the forces interlinking and dramatically affecting life on planet Earth. Looking beyond the local community encourages us to recognize our role in global systems.

Note: Visit the following websites for some other regional issues to consider for discussion:
- Concentrated animal-feeding operations (visit www.epa.gov/guide/cafo, or http://www.sierraclub.org/water-sentinels)
- Colorado River (http://www.savethecolorado.org/)
- Grand Coulee Dam (visit www.dams.org)
- Delaware Estuary (visit http://water.epa.gov/type/oceb/nep/action.cfm)

Endnotes

1   Planetwire 2002 (E).
2   Wall 1998–2002 (E).
3   U.S. Environmental Protection Agency 2002 (E).
4   World Bank 2002 (E).
5   United Nations Population Fund 2002 (E).
6   PlanetWire.org 2002 (E).
7   Food and Agriculture Organization of the United Nations 2002 (E).
8   Wall 1998–2002 (E).
9   Ibid.
10 Paddock 1988 (B).
11 Wall 1998-2002 (E).
12 High Plains Underground Water Conservation District #1 2002 (E).
13 Texas Water Resources Institute 1998 (E).

Letters following author and date citations refer to sections in the bibliography (Appendix B) where the reader can find full data about the sources cited.

Getting Ready

- Before beginning the activity, ask students to visit a grocery store and list 10 items and where they originated. You might suggest that students start with the produce aisle or that they ask the produce manager about sources of the produce.
- Copy "Case Study: Ogallala Aquifer" (one per student), "Role #" (each student will be assigned one role), and "Shareholder's View" (one per student). *Note*: You don't have to assign all the roles provided. Feel free to pick and choose.

Doing the Activity

1. Invite students to share their lists of grocery store products (see "Getting Ready" above). How many items were local? How many were regional? How many came from another country? You might also ask students to look at products that they are using (e.g., pens, notebooks) or at their clothing to see where the materials that make up those items came from and where the items were manufactured. Help students start thinking about the implications of the regional and global nature of commerce and how that nature affects community connections.

2. Explain that students will be challenged to seek solutions to a real-world problem. Distribute "Case Study: Ogallala Aquifer" for students to read. Although the Ogallala Aquifer is in the Great Plains, its water resources help to produce the food that many of us eat, no matter where in the United States we live.

3. Ask students, "Who would you expect to be concerned about the depletion of the Ogallala Aquifer? Why?"

4. Explain that students will be participants in the Ogallala Aquifer Multistate Summit. Students will adopt the role of a **shareholder** in the Ogallala region and will work in teams to negotiate an action plan. Review the following instructions:

- Each team will be composed of six to eight different shareholders.
- Working in their teams, students will adopt shareholders' roles, debate views, and develop a team resolution.
- Each team will assign a note taker to record key points and will designate one or more speakers to present the team's action plan to the rest of the class.

5. Consider discussing tips to ensure fair listening (e.g., not interrupting, looking at the speaker, writing down questions to return to later, rephrasing or echoing other people's ideas, finding a point of agreement before pointing out differences, being respectful, refraining from personal comments, requesting clarification, and speaking in a calm and even tone). List those tips on the board. Ask students to use the guidelines in their team discussions.

6. Assemble students into teams of six to eight students. Give each student, on each team, a different "Role #."

7. Distribute copies of "Shareholder's View" for students to complete. The sheet is designed to help students adopt their roles and to serve as an assessment tool.

8. Ask students to read quietly and fill out items 1–4 on the "Shareholder's View" sheet from the perspective of their assigned character. They will fill out item 5 after they have discussed the issue with their team members.

9. Have students introduce themselves in character to the other members of their team and mention where they are from.

10. Have students adopt their roles and discuss the Ogallala Aquifer issue. Each team should build a consensus on how to handle the problem. Remind students that compromise may be necessary. In rare cases, an innovative solution might meet everyone's needs and offer a win–win situation. Rather than having them focus on the characters' differences, encourage teams to focus on the common ground. Guiding questions

might include these: Is there a common concern shared by everyone? Is there an action you would all like to see? On which points can you all agree?

11. Instruct the note taker to record the team's commonalities, individual views, and possible solutions. Teams should ensure that the "speaker" understands the notes. Remind teams to ask for assistance if they reach an impasse.

12. During team discussions, rotate and record notes about each team's cooperation and focus.

13. Invite each team to present its solution to the rest of the class.

14. After each presentation, ask audience members to write a few notes offering the team constructive feedback about the presentation and the information presented. Collect all notes at the end of class.

15. Draw on the following questions to debrief the activity:
- What challenges did teams face in trying to reach consensus? How were they overcome?
- What were the major sources of disagreement?
- What issues could not be resolved? Why?
- Did any of the shareholders dominate the discussion?
- How did the different solutions deal with the regional nature of the issue?
- How does the issue of the Ogallala Aquifer in the Great Plains affect the rest of the nation? Your community?
- What are some issues in your community that involve shareholders? Who are the players?
- Does sense of place affect one's point of view? Did it cause conflict or disagreement? How did it influence the summit and action plan?

Enrichment

- Have students investigate a current regional issue involving their community, possibly concerning water use. Their research should address the players, their positions, the problem, their different beliefs and values, and the possible solutions. Students might use the "Shareholder's View" page for guidance. For an added challenge, encourage students to compare the Ogallala issue to their selected local issue. Students can continue tracking the issue over time to see how it develops and resolves.

- Encourage students to research current updates on the Ogallala issue. How do the real events compare to the teams' action plan ideas?

- Where does your community's water originate? What is the source of the water that flows when students turn on the tap at home or in school? Who do you think uses the most water in your community? For what purposes? Invite students to research and learn more about water use in their community. This undertaking might include a field trip to a local reservoir, wetland, or pumping station.

- Ask students to track their water use for a day or a week. How does their use compare to the national per capita average of 578 liters per day? Are there simple ways to reduce water use? What are the benefits of water conservation? What are the challenges?

- Water has played a significant role in the development of many cities in the southwest. Use the video *Making Sense of Place - Phoenix: The Urban Desert*, a one-hour documentary film about Phoenix, Arizona which has expanded from a small desert town to the sixth largest city in the United States in just 50 years. The film explores the interrelationships both caused by and affecting individual choices, the democratic process and market forces in the region. For further information go to: www.makingsenseofplace.com

Case Study: Ogallala Aquifer

Do you use Ogallala water? The underground Ogallala Aquifer, also known as the High Plains Aquifer, once held as much water as Lake Huron (three billion acre-feet*). If pumped out over the United States, the aquifer would cover all 50 states with one and one-half feet of water. The aquifer is like a bucket full of wet gravel with all the pore spaces filled with water and a bedrock seal on the bottom. As the largest groundwater system in North America, the aquifer runs under parts of eight states: southern South Dakota, eastern Wyoming, most of Nebraska, eastern Colorado, western Kansas, western Oklahoma, western Texas, and eastern New Mexico.

Figure 1 Ogallala Aquifer

Source: North Plains Groundwater Conservation District

When the practice of irrigation became popular after World War II, people believed the Ogallala was an inexhaustible resource fed from an underground river originating in the Rocky Mountains. Farmers and landowners pumped extravagant amounts of water without any thought of conservation. A fourfold rise in use occurred between 1940 and 1970. By the 1970s, the Ogallala watered one-fifth of the total land under irrigation in the United States. Today, approximately 95 percent of the water pumped from the aquifer is devoted to irrigation. The water irrigates crops such as alfalfa, corn, cotton, and wheat, much of which is used to feed livestock.

The shaded area on the map represents the aquifer (see Figure 1): When the aquifer started to show signs of depletion, communities across state lines began negotiating. University of Kansas reported that "Farmers around Sublette, Kansas, figured in 1970 they had about 300 years of water left. In 1980 they reckoned they had 70 years' supply; in 1990, less than 30. Half the accessible water was gone by 1993.... While it took many millennia to fill, the Ogallala's usefulness to humankind will almost surely last less than a century."

*An acre-foot is equivalent to the volume of water required to cover 1 acre to a depth of 1 foot.

Case Study: Ogallala Aquifer (cont.)

Regional decision makers continue to struggle with the issue. They face the dual challenges of continued growth and economic dependence on the resource. To date, people have not limited their use of the aquifer to sustainable levels. Instead, citizens have pumped out water faster than it can be replenished. The Ogallala holds fossil water, which is water that has accumulated over the past 10,000 to 25,000 years. The only method of recharging this aquifer is the slow percolation of water through the soil. Because most of the High Plains soils are not very porous, recharging may occur at a rate of only an inch or so per year.

Ogallala water supports a significant portion of the nation's food supply. Yet, far too many people rely on greater groundwater yields than would be possible with the natural recharge rate. Farmers drained the aquifer at a rate of 1 percent per year in the late 1970s, drawing water 10 times faster than the aquifer could recharge under the best conditions. From the 1940s to 1980, the aquifer declined an average of 10 feet, with some areas in Texas declining nearly 100 feet. However, during the 1980s, the aquifer declined only another foot because of improved irrigation practices and new technologies. According to water scientists at the Kansas

Geological Survey, about 40 percent of the aquifer should be able to support pumping for the next 100 years, if water is used at the 1978–98 rate of withdraw. (Data for the remaining area of the aquifer were incomplete; therefore, the team at KGS was unable to project depletion rates for the entire aquifer.) To view maps of water level changes in the Ogallala Aquifer, go to http://ne.water.usgs.gov.

Sources:
Guru and Horne 2005 (E).
McNeill 2000 (A).
Romanek 1997 (E).
Texas Water Resources Institute 1998 [1978] (E).
University of Kansas 2001 (E).

Role #1—Citizens Alliance for the Aquifer

Concern #1—The Citizens Alliance for the Aquifer (CAA) has several concerns regarding managing the Ogallala Aquifer CAA is a consortium of more than 1,500 individuals and businesses from several states in the High Plains region. Our consortium's mission is to hear—and to represent to public officials—the concerns of citizens throughout the region.

The following is a summary of the multiple issues that we believe must be taken into account as a multistate resolution is sought:

- Multistate cooperation with regard to the remaining resources of the Ogallala Aquifer
- Scientific research on the ecological repercussions of artificial groundwater recharge using reclaimed wastewater
- Economic incentives for sustainable practices
- Locally enforceable regulation (because the region is too large for regulation by a few federal agents)
- Ecological impact statements on the effects of aquifer mining on wildlife
- Increased access to the *playa* lakes for recreational purposes (e.g., game bird hunting)
- Subsidies to offset economic losses of farmers who must dig deeper for water
- Monitoring of feedlots to reduce nitrogen waste seepage and pesticide seepage
- For new construction, impact fees that are based on projected water usage of new households
- Full-scale assessment (e.g., feasibility, available markets) of drought-tolerant crops
- Federal assistance to offset the rising cost of drilling for water
- Equity in subsidies for all farmers or incentives for water-use reductions
- A framework of regular communications with citizens

Role #2—Colorado High School Student

Concern #2—I think we need to stop wasting the remaining water and to find out what it would take to let the aquifer recharge.

The Ogallala Aquifer once held enough water to fill Lake Huron. However, we are using the water faster than it is being replenished. In some places, the aquifer is almost empty. Once drained, the aquifer will take an estimated 6,000 years to refill. Agriculture is the primary drain on the aquifer and is the topic we need to focus on while seeking a solution to the overuse problem.

The Ogallala Aquifer, which stretches from Texas to South Dakota, is the main source of water for all the High Plains. The aquifer is being depleted at an alarming rate in many areas. At current use rates, the aquifer will be dry in 30 or 40 years. That is during my lifetime!

I have read that many farmers are using inefficient watering methods. They use sprinklers that spray water from such heights that much of it evaporates before it reaches the plants. Farmers who irrigate with ditches pour too much water onto the crops, and the excess water sits there until it evaporates.

Some solutions for those wasteful practices are readily available. Because the water evaporates from the high sprinklers before reaching the crops, why not install lower sprinklers? If the water is closer to the plants, less will evaporate. To keep from wasting water in ditch irrigating, the farmer could buy gypsum blocks, which are a valuable device that is buried in the ground near the roots to monitor available soil moisture. With this method, you can always tell how much water you are using and how much water you need. Given the status of water resources, there is no excuse for wasting any.

Unless methods for conserving water are implemented in the High Plains, the water supply could run out in a matter of years, which would be an undesirable outcome not only for the farmers but also for those of us who depend on their produce for food.

I do not understand why nothing is being done when we know about this problem and that it is only getting worse. What if the water is gone by the time I am 50? What will I do? Will I have to move away? What about all the families who live in the High Plains states? Will everyone have to move? A lot of people can't afford to just move—the poorest will be left behind. We need to redefine the agricultural industry, keeping the jobs but stopping the wasting of water. What about all the people in the United States who rely on beef and grain from the High Plains? What will happen if the industry falls apart in 50 years? We need to produce food on our own land here in the United States so that we are not dependent on foreign countries. Depending on foreign food would make us very vulnerable as a nation. Does everyone realize how important this matter is? I am eager to do what I can to work toward a solution; that is why I came to this summit.

Sources:
www.bvsd.k12.co.us
Based on a student letter by L. Thompson.
www.conservewy.com

Role #3—Ecologist from Nebraska

Concern #3—I believe we threaten our species and others by disturbing the web of life that we don't fully understand. We're all connected.

The loss of water from the aquifer is not just about humans running out of water for their use. The repercussions affect the wider ecological community. Underground water reserves are connected to aboveground water sources. We need to look at the entire system when considering the environmental impacts of depleting this resource. When withdrawals exceed recharge rates, the result is lower water tables and (often in the summer) slower, lower, and warmer streams.

Those factors affect species living in the streams. Insect larvae are a critical link in the stream food web. Those and other species are extremely sensitive to variables like temperature, nutrient concentrations, contaminants such as pesticides, dissolved oxygen, and flow rate. Less water in streams reduces habitat for species and impairs water quality. When streams run too slowly, creatures that depend on the flushing of contaminants such as pesticides can be poisoned. When streams run too low, creatures that have grown dependent on higher rates cannot survive.

I am particularly concerned about trout. Higher water temperatures in the summer reduce reproduction rates. The fish depend on groundwater contributions to stream flow; the temperature of the groundwater keeps their eggs from overheating in summer and from freezing in winter. Groundwater and waters on the surface are intimately connected; I doubt that we have even begun to understand the complexity and interrelationships of the system. In this semiarid climate, the impacts of depleting groundwater resources are likely magnified.

My point is simple. Groundwater moves toward and connects to water on the surface. Ecology is about systems. When we try to divide up issues and are not seeing them in context, or as a whole, we make mistakes. Our knowledge is limited, so we must use all we know to make the best possible decisions. We can't ignore "minor details." For example, eliminating trout habitat doesn't just affect recreational fishing. Simply put, if trout are affected, other species will be also. And speaking personally, I believe that trout are valuable simply because they are trout. I do not want a world where fish do not swim free in our rivers. They are a part of my quality of life; my health and well-being are tied to theirs.

Source:
Jackson et al. 2001 (B).

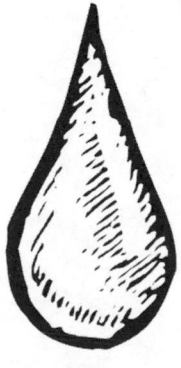

Role #4—Meat Industry Representative from Texas

Concern #4—Folks, millions of people rely on Ogallala water, including my company's employees and their families, the farmers of the High Plains, and most meat-eating Americans. The economy of the region depends on the aquifer's water. Restricting our ability to pump water will cause financial problems for many of us.

Most of the water pumped from the Ogallala is used to irrigate crops, much of which are grown to feed livestock. Throughout the 1980s and 1990s, the largest beef-packing company of the High Plains increased employment from 9,500 to 52,000 people, and sales grew from $4.6 billion to $16.9 billion. In October 2001, the company merged with the world's largest poultry producer, making it the nation's largest meat-packing company. The company, which processes beef, pork, and poultry, now claims the largest percentage of the U.S. market, serving as the nation's (and perhaps the world's) largest beef processor. I represent the company.

The previous chief executive officer of this company based in the High Plains also served on the board of directors for several organizations, including a federal reserve bank, a major energy company, a petroleum corporation, and the National Livestock and Meat Board. Clearly, the meat industry is big business in the United States, and upper-level meat industry executives are major players on the national and international business scene.

My company now provides thousands of jobs across the United States, keeps meat and grain farms in business, and feeds the nation. We have been a responsible neighbor, constructing wastewater treatment systems to reduce ammonia discharge into the Missouri River and resolving water quality issues at former facilities in Texas.

Source:
Center for Study of Responsive Law, 2005 (E).

Role #5—Farmer from Kansas

Concern #5—Mostly what I want people here to keep in mind is that the sustainable farming practices have not been proven over generations to not harm farmers' livelihood, and I simply cannot afford to take that risk with my operation.

My family relies on support payments from the government. With the federal economic incentives, we can turn a profit and make a living. Federal programs do not recognize the crop rotation system that the sustainable agriculture folks propose. My family would receive nothing if I implemented those suggestions. You all seem to have this nostalgic attachment to the American farmer, but then you don't seem to know one when you're looking at her or him. My family has farmed this land for generations, and my students are learning to farm this land after me. We maintain the way of life you say is being lost in this country, so I don't understand why you aren't willing to provide more support for the regular farmer who can't afford to take the risks you suggest.

I represent the people who are the backbone of this region's economy. Let's not forget what this issue is about. Families, cities, entire states, and a nation depend on our grain and meat industries. If I switched to more sustainable practices, I understand that for the first few years I would likely have lower yields. I am aware that this approach might be offset by the costs of fertilizers and pesticides, but it is still a risk. I barely make a living some years as it is. You say there is little difference—even with increased labor costs—but, again, I can't take that risk.

Don't get me wrong; I am interested in the increased water-holding capacity of sustainable practices. But I have already invested in a large-scale irrigation system and can hardly imagine running drip irrigation lines across all those acres! Farming is a business. There's no time to do all that by hand. If I didn't have a family to support, maybe I could take more risks. Someday in the future, maybe my students will have to grow wheat or farm some new way because pumping the water will be too expensive.

I say, "No more regulations on farmers." We aren't the ones overpopulating this region. What about all those people watering their lawns and golf courses? What about all the people eating the food we produce? Farmers cost the government less per acre than suburban people. We don't need the infrastructure that they do. In the suburbs, water and sewer lines run to every house, on every quarter of an acre. Has anyone compared water use per acre on farms to the use in the suburbs? Why do people want to blame farmers so fast? Maybe they don't want to look at their own way of living. I don't mean to offend anyone; I just want fair representation for farmers.

Source:
Guru and Horne 2005 (E).

Role #6—Agricultural Engineer from Wyoming

Concern #6—We need to think about the long-term sustainability and environmental impacts of water use in this globally significant agricultural area.

The Ogallala Aquifer, underlying half a million square kilometers of the central United States, could be the largest aquifer in the world. Although figures vary, it is estimated that the aquifer provides 20 percent to 30 percent of the total groundwater used for irrigation in the United States. It also provides domestic water to approximately 80 percent of the 2.3 million residents of the region. About 40 percent of those people live in the region's 10 largest cities. The region is a globally significant agricultural production area. More than half the land (54 percent) is used for agriculture. Wheat, cotton, and corn grown here amount to 15 percent to 20 percent of the total of each crop grown in the United States.

Eighteen percent of the cattle in the United States and a growing percentage of swine are also produced here. In 1995, regional water use for irrigation and meat processing amounted to almost 20 billion gallons per day. One-fifth came from surface waters (85 percent of which came from the Platte River in Nebraska), and four-fifths came from aquifers. Excluding the Platte River, 92 percent of the water used in the High Plains is supplied by groundwater, and about 95 percent of this water irrigates crops. The rest is used for domestic drinking water, livestock, mining, and industry, in that order.

Regional water-quality issues of concern include the following:

- Nutrient enrichment or pollution of groundwater from the operations of feeding confined animals
- Effects of agricultural and urban land use practices on general groundwater quality—specifically, the potential degradation of drinking water
- Deterioration of groundwater quality as a result of infiltration of degraded surface water
- Effects of focused recharge through *playa* lakes on local groundwater quality

Groundwater is being depleted globally because, in some areas, it takes centuries to recharge. Some aquifers are rechargeable, but others that contain fossil waters that had been formed when the Pleistocene ice sheets melted are considered a nonrenewable resource. Rates of recharge vary widely, from hundreds to tens of thousands of years. Some scientists consider the Ogallala to be nonrenewable. It does not recharge quickly enough to sustain current use levels. By the 1970s, farmers were already draining the aquifer 10 times faster than the recharge rate in some areas. For nonrenewable groundwater sources, sustainable or appropriate rates of extraction are difficult issues to discuss. Almost any extraction may be nonsustainable, and appropriate rates of extraction are difficult—if not impossible—to determine. At what rate should groundwater pumping be allowed? For what purpose? And who, if anyone, will safeguard the needs of future generations? In the Ogallala Aquifer, for example, the water may be lowered significantly over the next century.

Source:
Jackson et al. 2001 (B).

Role #7—Toxicologist from Nebraska

Concern #7—Poor agricultural practices are contaminating the water quality of the aquifer.

The Ogallala Aquifer's water supply is being depleted at alarming rates. At the same time, the remaining water quality is becoming increasingly polluted because of poor agricultural practices. Agricultural runoff is the greatest nonpoint source of water pollution in the United States. Salt, fertilizers, pesticides, chemicals, and animal wastes are contaminating the aquifer and consequently affecting soil productivity and our health.

Unlike municipal or sewage water, irrigation does not permit improvement of water quality before it returns to the source. This situation leads to changes in the amounts of dissolved salts and adds agricultural chemicals and eroded sediments to both the soil and the aquifer. For instance, nitrates found in the fertilizers used on farms and home lawns seep into groundwater; that water can be harmful when consumed by children and pregnant women. Pesticides have also seeped into groundwater; in some areas, they have exceeded water quality standards established by the Environmental Protection Agency. There are no known economical ways to remove the pesticides once they have entered groundwater sources. Animal wastes from confined feeding operations of cattle, hogs, and chicken are another major source of water pollution, which, in turn, decreases the soil's productivity.

The water of the Ogallala Aquifer is generally still suitable for irrigation. However, levels of dissolved solids or salts, fluoride, chloride, and sulfate are above the EPA's drinking water standards. Federal monitoring occurs in any community that relies on groundwater for drinking, but in other areas, such monitoring is infrequent or nonexistent because of the associated high costs.

Better management and monitoring are needed to help safeguard the water quality of the Ogallala Aquifer and to ensure that future generations can safely use the water for drinking and irrigation.

Source:
Guru and Horne 2005 (E).

Role #8—Economist from South Dakota

Concern #8—Conserving the Ogallala Aquifer is essential to the economy of the High Plains.

The economy of the High Plains is centered on three sectors: crops, livestock, and meat processing. Each of those sectors is highly dependent on water drawn from the Ogallala Aquifer. Irrigated crops provide food for livestock, which, in turn, is the primary input for meat-processing plants. Because of the aquifer's slow rate of recharge, the High Plains economy relies on a finite resource.

Water is fundamental to the region's livelihood, and policies affecting water use ultimately change the scope and distribution of economic activity, plus the use of land and other natural resources. For instance, the U.S. Department of Agriculture's Farm Service Agency instituted the Conservation Reserve Program in 1985. This voluntary program, which is available to agricultural producers, helps protect environmentally sensitive land. Participants plant long-term, resource-conserving groundcover to improve water quality, to control soil erosion, and to enhance wildlife habitat. This method reduces water runoff and sedimentation and, therefore, protects both groundwater and water on the surface. In return, participants receive rental payments and other financial assistance.

Legislators should focus on the economics of water conservation when drafting new policy initiatives. We must conserve for economic efficiency, which means that resource use should yield the greatest net benefit to society. However, private costs of pumping are less than the social costs of withdrawing water—so excessive pumping occurs. Colorado, Kansas, and New Mexico have adopted policies to deny new water permits if water availability in surrounding wells would be significantly reduced. However, no such restrictions occur in Texas, where the Texas Supreme Court ruled that "the owner of the land is the absolute owner of the soil and percolating water."

Sources:
Peterson, Marsh, and Williams 2003 (B).
U.S. Department of Agriculture Farm Service Agency 2003 (E).

Shareholder's View

Fill in the sheet below from the perspective of your assigned role.

Role: _____

1. Problem (what is at risk?):

2. Issue (a point or matter of discussion, debate, or dispute):

3. Players and Position:

4. Values or beliefs:

5. What are you willing to negotiate?

6. Possible solutions:

Notes

Appendix A

Glossary

Affordable housing—shelter that requires a household to pay 30 percent or less of its annual income on housing.

Aquifer—porous, water-saturated layers of sand, gravel, or bedrock that can yield an economically significant amount of water.

Big-box stores—national or regional chain stores—usually 100,000 square feet or more in area—that sell a variety of merchandise at discounted prices.

Biodiversity—the number and variety of organisms found within a specified geographic region.

Biota—the combined flora and fauna of a region or period

Brownfield—with certain legal exclusions and additions, the term "brownfield site" means real property, the expansion, redevelopment, or reuse of which may be complicated by the presence or potential presence of a hazardous substances, pollutants, or contaminants.

Built environment—highways, homes, industrial areas, parks, roads, schools, waste disposal sites, and workplaces that are modified by people.

Community—living and nonliving components such as animals, plants, humans, waterways, and buildings, all coexisting and interacting with one another.

Community character—although this term lacks a singular definition, it refers to the unique qualities of a community and the attributes that help give those people living there a sense of place; key components include the community's cultural, historic characteristics, natural, and visual.

Compact development—use of as little land as possible for development, thus minimizing the impacts on the environment; further, the development limits urban movement into rural areas by revitalizing and efficiently using the existing land within urban areas.

Comprehensive management plan—a plan for development of an area that recognizes the aesthetic, economic, physical, political, social, and related factors of the community involved.

Conservation easement—designed to exclude certain activities on private land such as commercial development or residential subdivisions, its primary purpose is to conserve natural or built resources on the land; it also gives the holder the responsibility to monitor and enforce property restrictions imposed by the easement for as long as it is designed to run. (An easement does not grant ownership nor does it absolve the property owner from the traditional owner responsibilities such as property tax, upkeep, maintenance, or improvements.)

Designer—one who directs the change, conservation, and growth of an area.

Ecological footprint—the measure of how much land and water area a human population needs to produce the resources required to sustain itself and to absorb its wastes, given prevailing technology.

Environmental quality—the health or state of natural resources such as air, minerals, soil, vegetation, and water.

Gentrification—displacement of lower-income city dwellers who are frequently linked to older manufacturing businesses by higher-income professionals who work in the service and information industries.

Geographic Information System (GIS)—a combination of elements designed to store, retrieve, manipulate, and display geographic data about places; a GIS package comprises four basic parts: robust hardware, powerful software, spatial data, and a thinking explorer. (A GIS manages location-based information and provides the tools to display and analyze it, whether the information relates to population characteristics, economic development opportunities, or vegetation types.)

Green infrastructure—a strategically planned and managed network of conservation easements, greenways, parks, wilderness, and working lands with conservation value that supports native species, maintains natural ecological processes, sustains air and water resources, and contributes to the health and quality of life for America's communities and people.

Green space—an area with most of its area not in concrete or asphalt; land that consists predominantly of unsealed, permeable, "soft" surfaces such as soil, grass, shrubs, and trees and may include all areas of parks, play areas, and other green spaces specifically intended for recreational use, plus other green spaces with other origins.

Groundwater—water that occurs under the ground in layers of sand, gravel, and other unconsolidated material.

Invasive species—a plant, animal, or other organism that is typically nonnative (or alien) to a particular ecosystem and whose introduction causes—or is likely to cause—harm to the economy, the environment, or human health. (Killer bees and water hyacinth are two examples of invasive species.)

Land trust—a private, tax-exempt, nonprofit corporation that seeks to preserve land through land acquisition or land donations; land trusts often provide the local leadership, commitment, and flexibility essential for local resources protection and growth management efforts. (The trusts offer continuity of management and monitoring of valuable natural resources.)

Land use—development of land for agricultural, commercial, industrial, recreational, residential, or other purposes.

Land use planning—the systematic assessment of land and water potential; alternative patterns of land use; and other economic, physical, and social conditions for the purpose of selecting and adopting land use options that are most

beneficial to land users without degrading the resources or the environment, together with the selection of measures that are most likely to encourage such land uses. (Land-use planning may be at international, national, district, or local levels; it includes participation by land users, planners, and decision makers and covers educational, financial, fiscal, and legal measures.

Mass transit—municipal or regional publicly shared transportation, such as buses, ferries, streetcars, and trains, which are open to all riders on a nonreserved basis.

Metropolitan—a large population nucleus of 50,000 or greater, together with adjacent communities that have a high degree of social and economic integration with that core.

Mixed-use neighborhoods—communities that have land uses with complementary functions that are located close together; complementary uses may include housing, movie theaters, offices, restaurants, and shopping—destinations to which people travel on a regular basis.

Open space—land that is not developed; a term that is often used interchangeably with the term "green space."

Ordinance—a local law.

Place—an area with definite or indefinite boundaries; a locality, such as a town or city.

Planner—one who formulates plans and policies to meet the economic, physical, and social needs of communities, and who develops the strategies to make those plans work.

Planning—the goal within cities and regions of furthering the common good of people and their communities by creating attractive, convenient, efficient, equitable, and healthful environments for present and future generations.

Prime farmland—land that has the best combination of chemical and physical characteristics for producing crops and that is also available for those uses. (It is the best land for growing crops but may include land not currently being used for crops.)

Public health—the focus on preventing disease, injury, and premature death by taking a population-based approach to addressing root causes of health issues. (Lifestyle and environment have the greatest effects on one's health.)

Quality of life—a concept that roughly refers to living a good life while defining that what is "good" can be a difficult task because the quality-of-life concept changes over time and place and can mean different things to different people and cultures. (Although it is impossible to give a singular and definitive meaning to the term, it is possible to understand quality of life as a framework in which people distinguish living from living well.)

Scenic—constituting or affording pleasing views of natural features.

Scenic viewshed—the area within one's sight from a designated location that offers pleasing views of natural features.

Sense of place—is a special collection of qualities and characteristics, visual, cultural, social, and environmental that provides meaning to location. Sense of place is the factor that makes an environment psychologically comfortable.

Shareholder—individual or group having an interest in the outcome of a particular issue, problem, or question.

Smart growth—development that serves the community, the economy, and the environment. (See Appendix E for more details.)

Social capital—the stock of active connections among people, that is, the trust, mutual understanding, and shared values and behaviors that bind the members of human networks and communities and that make cooperative action possible.

Social infrastructure—the critical, underlying framework of a community's social environment.

Sprawl—spread-out patterns of development; the area taken up by a large or expanding development or city; or growth outward without filling in the areas closer to the city center.

Topographic—referring to the graphic representation of the surface features of a place or region on a map, indicating their relative positions and elevations.

Traditional neighborhood—a term used in a planning context to describe a pattern of mixed-use and pedestrian-friendly communities that may also provide a variety of housing types, attractive public and green spaces, homes with front porches, and compact design.

Tragedy of the commons—the concept that property held in common by many people will generally be overused until it deteriorates or is even destroyed; a "commons" is any resource that is used as though it belongs to all. (In other words, when someone can use a shared resource simply because one wants or needs to use it, then one is using a commons.)

Transit-oriented development—land use that promotes high-density housing, retail, employment opportunities, and other services in a concentrated area in close proximity (usually about one-fourth of a mile) of transit stations.

Urban—referring to a densely settled territory with a population of 50,000 or more inhabitants.

Urban design—the process of giving physical direction to urban growth, conservation, and change. (Urban design includes landscape as well as buildings—both preservation and new construction—plus rural areas as well as cities.)

Urban forest—the sum of all woody and associated vegetation in and around dense human settlements, ranging from small communities in rural settings to metropolitan regions. (The forest is the sum of park trees, greenbelt vegetation, residential trees, and street trees; it includes trees on unused public and private land, trees in transportation and utility corridors, and forests on watershed lands.)

Urban growth boundary—a line drawn around a city that prohibits development outside that boundary. These boundaries are designed to accommodate growth by slowing or preventing sprawl for a designated period of time and are used to guide infrastructure development.

Visioning—a process in which participants focus on what they see as *desirable*, rather than on what they think is *possible*, and they imagine improvements that they would personally like to see happen to create a better future.

Visual character—qualities that one can see and that define or distinguish a community.

Visual pollution—elements that are in a community and are deemed undesirable to see.

Watershed—a geographic area of land bounded by topographic features that drains waters to a shared destination; it also captures precipitation, filters and stores water, and determines its release. (Within the watershed, many distinctive biotic and abiotic components function interrelatedly.)

Wildland–urban interface—the area where human development (homes and other buildings) meets undeveloped wildland or vegetative fuels, such as branches, dead leaves, shrubs, trees, and twigs.

Zoning—a land-use classification system that establishes a range of permissible development options for a piece of property. (Zoning establishes what legally can and cannot occur on a given property.)

Endnotes

Sources for glossary terms:
Altenhof 1999 (E).
American Planning Association 2003 (E)
Barnett 1982 (A).
Besser 1995 (E).
Columbia Encyclopedia 2000 (E).
Dictionary.com 2003 (E).
Dohm 1999 (A).
Environmental Health Perspective Online 2002 (E).
Environmental Science Systems and Solutions 2003 (E).
Environmental Systems Research Institute 1998 (C).
European Environment Agency 1993 (E)
Fisheries and Oceans Canada 2003 (E).
Fort Worth 2003 (E)
Georgia Department of Community Affairs (E).
Gillham 2002 (A).
GreenInfrastructure.Net 2002a (E).
Gunnett, Swanwick, and Woolley 2002 (E).
Invasivespecies.gov 2003 (E).
Maryland Department of Natural Resources 2003 (E).
Miller 1996 (E).
Ohio State University 2003 (E).
Preservation Alliance of Virginia 2003 (E).
Project Learning Tree 1994 (A).
Smith 2002 (E).
U.S. Census Bureau 2001 (E).
U.S. Department of Housing and Urban Development 2003 (E).
U.S. Environmental Protection Agency 2002 (E).

Letters following author and date citations refer to sections in the bibliography (Appendix B) where the reader can find full data about the sources cited.

Appendix B

Bibliography

(A) Books

Barnett, Jonathan. *An Introduction to Urban Design*. New York: Harper & Row, 1982.

Beatley, Timothy, and Kristy Manning. *The Ecology of Place*. Washington, DC: Island Press, 1997.

Benfield, F. Kaid, Jukta Terris, and Nancy Vorsanger. *Solving Sprawl: Models of Smart Growth in Communities Across America*. New York: Natural Resources Defense Council, 2001.

Benfield, F. Kaid, Matthew D. Raimi, and Donald D. T. Chen. *Once There Were Greenfields*. New York: Natural Resources Defense Council, 1999.

Bollier, David. *How Smart Growth Can Stop Sprawl*. Washington, DC: Essential Books, 1998.

Campbell, John. *Map Use and Analysis*. 4th ed. New York: McGraw-Hill, 2001.

Center for Study of Representative Law, P.O. Box 19367, Washington, DC 20036.

Columbia Encyclopedia. 6th ed. New York: Columbia University Press, 2000. www.questia.com.

Dohm, Richard R. *Handbook for Planning Commissioners in Missouri*. Columbia: University of Missouri, 1999.

Duany, Andres, Elizabeth Plater-Zyberk, and Jeff Speck. *Suburban Nation: The Rise of Sprawl and the Decline of the American Dream*. New York: North Point Press, 2000.

Eblen, Ruth A., and William R. Eblen. *The Encyclopedia of the Environment*. Boston: Houghton Mlin, 1994.

Friedman, Avi. *Planning the New Surburbia: Flexibility by Design*. Vancouver, BC: University of British Columbia Press, 2002.

Gallagher, Winifred. *The Power of Place*. New York: Harper Perennial, 1993.

Gillham, Oliver. *The Limitless City: A Primer on the Urban Sprawl Debate*. Washington, DC: Island Press, 2002.

Hall, Kenneth B., and Gerald A. Porterfield. *Community by Design: New Urbanism for Suburbs and Small Communities*. New York: McGraw-Hill, 2001.

Harnik, Peter. *Inside City Parks*. Washington, DC: Trust for Public Land and the Urban Land Institute, 2000.

Hart, Roger. *Childrens Participation*. London: Earthscan Publications, 1997.

Hiss, Tony. *The Experience of Place*. New York: Knopf, 1990.

Hough, Michael. *City Form and Natural Process*. New York: Routledge, 1995.

Howe, Jim, Ed McMahon, and Luther Propst. *Balancing Nature and Commerce in Gateway Communities*. Washington, DC: Island Press, 1997.

Jacbos, Jane. *The Death and Life of Great American Cities*. New York: Random House, Inc. 1961. Renewed 1989.

Kingsley, G. Thomas, Claudia J. Coulton, Michael Barndt, David S. Sawicki, and Peter Tatian. *Mapping Your Community: Using Geographic Information to Strengthen Community Initiatives*. Washington, DC: U.S. Department of Housing and Urban Development, 1997.

Knowles, Anne Kelly, ed. *Past Time, Past Place: GIS for History*. Redlands, CA: ESRI Press, 2002.

Kunstler, James Howard. *The Geography of Nowhere*. New York: Simon and Schuster, 1994.

Langdon, Philip. *A Better Place to Live: Reshaping the American Suburb*. Amherst, MA: University of Massachusetts Press, 1994.

Leach, William. *Country of Exiles: The Destruction of Place in American Life*. New York: Vintage Books, 1999.

Leopold, Aldo. *A Sand County Almanac*. London: Oxford University Press, 1949.

McGregor, Gregor I. *Local Environmental Law, Land Use Control, and Limits to Government Power*. Boston: McGregor, Shea, and Doliner law firm, 1987.

McNeill, J. R. *Something New Under the Sun: An Environmental History of the Twentieth-Century World*. New York: W. W. Norton, 2000.

Miller, G. Tyler. *Living in the Environment*. 9th ed. Belmont, CA: Wordsworth Publishing, 1996.

Monmonier, Mark. *How to Lie with Maps*. Chicago: University of Chicago Press, 1996.

Mumford, Lewis. *The City in History*. New York: MJF Books, 1961.

Nabhan, Gary Paul, and Stephen A. Trimble. *The Geography of Childhood*. Boston: Beacon Press, 1995.

Orr, David. *Earth in Mind: On Education, Environment, and the Human Prospect*. Washington, DC: Island Press, 1994.

Project Learning Tree. *PreK–8 Environmental Education Activity Guide*. Washington, DC: American Forest Foundation, 1994.

Pyle, Robert Michael. *The Thunder Tree: Lessons from an Urban Wildland*. Boston: Houghton Mifflin, 1993.

Race, Bruce, and Carolyn Torma. *Youth Planning Charrettes: A Manual for Planners, Teachers, and Youth Advocates*. Chicago: American Planning Association, 1998.

Smith, Betty. *A Tree Grows in Brooklyn*. New York: Harper Collins, 1943.

Stegner, Wallace. *The Sense of Place*. New York: Random House, 1992.

Stroup, Richard. "Planning Versus Market Solutions." In *A Guide to Smart Growth: Shattering Myths, Providing Solutions*, edited by Jane S. Shaw and Ronald D. Utt. Washington, DC: Heritage Foundation and Political Economy Research Center, 2000.

Thoreau, Henry David. *Walden*. New York: New American Library, 1980.

Vallianatos, E. G. *Harvest of Devastation: The Industrialization of Agriculture and Its Human and Environmental Consequences*. New York: Apex Press, 1994.

[B] Journal, Magazine, and Newspaper Articles

Arnold, Henry. "Planning for Trees." *Planning Commissioners Journal* 2, (January/February 1992): 10–14.

Caballero, Vivienne. "The Human Footprint." *Wildlife Conservation* (February 2003): 14.

Cato Institute. "New Cato Study Refutes the Case for 'Smart Growth.'" *Cato Institute News Release*, January 24, 2000.

Cohen, Jack. "Preventing Disaster: Home Ignitability in the Wildlife–Urban Interface." *Journal of Forestry* 98, no. 3 (March 2000): 15–21.

Davenport, Coral. "In a fast-growing county, sprawl teaches hard lessons." *The Christian Science Monitor*, January 23, 2006.

Dietrich, William. "How Progress Ate America." *American Forests* (Autumn 1999): 24–29.

ENR Staff. "Redeveloping 25,000 Sites Would Create Jobs, Revenue." *ENR* 250, no. 23 (June 16, 2003): 23.

Frey, William H. "Escaping the City—and the Suburbs." *American Demographics* (June 2002).

Friedrich, Robert L., and Robert V. Blystone. "Internet Teaching Resources for Remote Sensing and GIS." *BioScience* 48, no. 3 (March 1998): 187–92.

Gordon, Peter, and Harry Richardson. "Critiquing Sprawl's Critics." *Cato Institute Policy Analysis* no. 365, January 24, 2000.

Jackson, Robert B., Stephen R. Carpenter, Clifford N. Dahm, Diane M. McKnight, Robert J. Naiman, Sandra L. Postel, and Steven W. Running. "Water in a Changing World." *Issues in Ecology* (Spring 2001): 2–16.

Kunstler, James. "Home From Nowhere." *The Atlantic Monthly* 278, no. 3 (September 1996): 43–50, 54–56, 61–66.

Kuo, F. E., and W. C. Sullivan. "Environment and Crime in the Inner City: Does Vegetation Reduce Crime?" *Environment and Behavior* 33, no. 3 (2001): 343–67.

Laris, Michael. "Loudoun Board Adopts Slow-Growth Zoning Blueprint." *Washington Post*, January 7, 2003, A1.

Laris, Michael, and Peter Whoriskey. "Loudoun's Ambitious Search for Perfection: County Aims to Keep Vast Acreage Rural." *Washington Post*, July 22, 2001, A1, A14–15.

McMahon, Ed. Quoted in "Greenways Specialist Explains Benefits of 'Green' Development" by Lisa Majors-Duff. *Sylvia Herald and Ruralite*, July 27, 2000.

Milligan, Jack. "Showdown in Loudoun: Smart Growers Battle Developers as One of the County's Fastest-Growing Counties Tries to Decide 'How Fast' and 'How Much.'" *US-Regional Newsline* 18, no. 4 (April 1, 2003): 8–13.

Nixon, Will. "How Nature Shapes Childhood." *Amicus* (Summer 1997): 31–35.

Paddock, Todd. "The Challenge of Protecting Groundwater." *Academy of Natural Sciences* (July 1988)

Pendered, David. "At Long Last, Day is Near: Atlantic Station to Open in April." *Atlanta Journal-Constitution*, March 29, 2004, Monday home edition, 1E.

Peterson, Jeffrey M., Thomas L. Marsh, and Jeffery R. Williams. "Conserving the Ogallala Aquifer: Efficiency, Equity, and Moral Motives." *Choices: The Magazine of Food, Farm, and Resource Issues* (February 2003).

Sanger, Matt. "Sense of Place and Education." *Journal of Environmental Education* 29, no. 1 (Fall 1997).

Smith, Gregory. "Coming Home: What Childhood Maps Reveal about the Experience of Place." *Clearing*. No. 96 (January/February 1997): 7–10.

Wong, Kathleen. "A Pixel Worth 1,000 Words." *U.S. News & World Report*, July 19, 1999, 48–50.

(C) Pamphlets/Reports/Newsletters

American Farmland Trust. "Fact Sheet: Why Save Farmland?" American Farmland Trust, Farmland Information Center, May 2002.

American Planning Association (APA). "Planning Communities for the 21st Century." Washington, DC: APA 1999.

Carnegie Mellon University, Department of Engineering and Public Policy, Department of Social and Decision Sciences, and H. J. Heinz III School of Public Policy and Management. "Pittsburgh's Urban Forest: Planting for the Future." Graduate Student Planning Project, Carnegie Mellon University, 1995.

Centers for Disease Control and Prevention, U.S. Department of Health and Human Services, "Active Community Environments." U.S. Department of Health and Human Services. Centers for Disease Control and Prevention, Washington, DC, June 2000.

Environmental Systems Research Institute. "GIS in K–12 Education." White Paper. Environmental Systems Research Institute, March 1998.

Ewing, Reid. *Pedestrian- and Transit-Friendly Design: A Primer for Smart Growth*. Washington, DC: Smart Growth Network/ICMA (International City/County Management Association), June 1999.

Haskin, Kathleen M. "Teaming GIS Technology with Experience-Based Lessons." *ArcNews* 24, no. 1 (Spring 2002): 37.

Holcombe, Randall G. "Live and Let Live." *PERC Reports*, February 1999.

Lerner, Steve, and William Poole. *The Economic Benefits of Parks and Open Space: How Land Conservation Helps Communities Grow Smart and Protect the Bottom Line*. Trust for Public Land, 1999.

O'Meara, Molly. "Reinventing Cities for People and the Planet." Worldwatch Paper 147, 1999.

Opie, John. "Is Sustainable Agriculture Possible in the Arid West? The Example of the Ogallala Aquifer." New Jersey Institute of Technology.

Oregon Transportation and Growth Management. *Commercial and Mixed-Use Development Code Handbook*, Portland, OR 2001.

Population Reference Bureau. *2004 World Population Data Sheet*. Washington, DC: Population Reference Bureau, 2004.

Riggs, David W. "The Anti-Sprawl Brigade's Poor Agenda." *CEI Update* 12, no. 11 (December 1999).

Smart Growth Network/ICMA. *Getting to Smart Growth: 100 Policies for Implementation*. Washington, DC: Smart Growth Network/ICMA, 2002.

Smart Growth Network/ICMA. *Why Smart Growth: A Primer*. Washington, DC: Smart Growth Network/ICMA, 1998.

State of Maryland. "Infill and Redevelopment." Draft. Annapolis, MD. State of Maryland, March 7, 2001.

United Nations. *World Urbanization Prospects: The 2003 Revision*. New York, NY. 2004.

U.S. Environmental Protection Agency. "Our Built and Natural Environments: A Technical Review of the Interactions Between Land Use, Transportation, and Environmental Quality." Washington, DC: Environmental Protection Agency, 2001.

(D) Curricula and Standards

Malone, Lyn, Anita M. Palmer, and Christine L. Voigt. *Mapping Our World: (GIS) Lessons for Educators*. Redlands, CA: Environmental Systems Research Institute Press, 2002.

National Geographic Research and Exploration. *Geography for Life: National Geography Standards*. Washington, DC: National Geographic Society, 1994.

The Dunn Foundation. *ViewFinders Too: Exploring Community Appearance*. Newport, Rhode Island: The Dunn Foundation, 2002.

(E) Internet Resources

All websites accessed April 30, 2015 except where noted.

About.com Guide. "Geography." http://geography.about.com

Altenhof, Laura. "Coping with Big Box Retailers." January, 1999. www.planning.org

American Forests. www.americanforests.org

American Forests. "What Is the National Urban Tree Deficit and Why Do We Care?" www.americanforests.org

American Forests. "Global ReLeaf." www.americanforests.org/our-programs/global-releaf-projects/

American Planning Association. "Urban and Regional Planning Career Information." www.planning.org

Ames, Steven C. "What Is Visioning? A Brief Introduction to the 'Oregon Model.'" Community Visioning. 2001. http://www.jfs.tku.edu.tw/wp-content/uploads/2014/01/152-S05.pdf

Ames, Steven C. "Community Visioning: Planning for the Future of Oregon's Local Communities." Arizona State University, College of Architecture and Environmental Design. 1997. www.asu.edu

Atlantic Station, LLP. "Life Happens Here." 2005. www.atlanticstation.com/concept.php

Australian Broadcasting Corporation. "Environmental Problems." Radio National, Ockham's Razor. February 7, 2000. www.abc.net.au

Beach, Dana. "Coastal Sprawl: The Effects of Urban Design on Aquatic Ecosystems in the United States." Pew Oceans Commission. 2002. www.pewtrusts.org

Besser, Terry L. "Do You Have a Social Infrastructure?" Iowa State University Extension. May 9, 1995. https://www.extension.iastate.edu/communities/news/ComCon07.html

Brittin, Rachel. "American Forests Unveils the 'National Urban Tree Deficit.'" September 5, 2001. www.americanforests.org/newsroom/

Benedict, Mark A., and Edward T. McMahon. "Green Infrastructure: Smart Conservation for the 21st Century." Sprawl Watch Clearinghouse. www.sprawlwatch.org/greeninfrastructure.pdf

Burns, Scott. "America's Stake in the Conservation of Fisheries and the Global Oceans." Economic Perspectives. January 2003. Economic Perspectives. http://photos.state.gov/libraries/korea/49271/dwoa_120909/ijee0103.pdf

Campbell, Robert. "A Social Alternative to Gridlock." Chicago BlueWays. *Boston Globe*, March 1, 2001.

Cato Institute. "New Cato Study Refutes the Case for 'Smart Growth.'" January 24, 2000. Cato Institute. www.cato.org

Center for Rural Pennsylvania. *Planning for the Future: A Handbook on Community Visioning.* 2nd ed., 2000. Available online at www.ruralpa.org/visioning.pdf

Center for Study of Responsive Law. 2005. www.csrl.org

Centers for Disease Control and Prevention. "Factors Contributing to Obesity." Modified May 2003. www.cdc.gov

City of Boulder, CO, Open Space and Mountain Parks. "Acquisition Program." www.bouldercolorado.gov (accessed January 24, 2002)

City of Tucson, AZ. "Livable Tucson Vision Program." June 27, 2000. www.ci.tucson.az.us

Columbia University, Center for International Earth Science Information Network (CIESIN). "Human Footprint." www.ciesin.columbia.edu/wild_areas

Community Resources. "Community Greening for Urban Revitalization." Programs and Projects—Baltimore. www.communityresources.org

Delaware Valley Regional Planning Commission. "Great Places with Transit." Summer/Fall 2001. www.pecpa.org (accessed January 7, 2002).

Dictionary.com. http://dictionary.reference.com

"DSNI Historic Timeline." 2002. Dudley Street Neighborhood Initiative. www.dsni.org

"Dudley Street Neighborhood Initiative." January 18, 2004. Dudley Street Neighborhood Initiative. www.dsni.org

Dunn Foundation. "ViewFinders Too Curriculum." www.dunnfoundation.org

Dunn Foundation. "ViewFinders Too Curriculum." www.dunnfoundation.org

Dunn, Madeline, Tito Montoya, and Bob White. "Albuquerque's Environmental Story." City of Albuquerque, NM. 2000. www.cabq.gov

Dwyer, John F., David J. Nowak, Mary Heather Noble, and Susan M. Sisinni. "Connecting People with Ecosystems in the 21st Century: An Assessment of Our Nation's Urban Forests." U.S. Department of Agriculture, Farm Service Agency. 2000. www.srs.fs.fed.us

Earthdaynetwork/Redefining Progress. "Ecological Footprint Quiz." http://files. earthday.net/footprint/index.html

EcoCity Cleveland. "Transportation Choices." www.gcbl.org

Environmental Defense Fund. "Scorecard." www.scorecard.org

Environmental Health Perspective Online. "Building Awareness of the Built Environment." October 23, 2003. http://www.ncbi.nlm.nih.gov/pmc/articles/ PMC1241081/

Environmental Protection Agency Green Book. "8-Hr Ozone Areas Listed by Area Name." June 15, 2004. http://www.epa.gov/ oaqps001/greenbk/map8hr.html

Environmental Science Systems and Solutions. "Interactive Glossary Definition." 2003. http://environment.jbpub.com/

Environmental Systems Research Institute (ESRI). "Industry Applications." www.esri.com/industries/index.html

Envision Utah. "Urban Planning Tools for Quality Growth." 1st ed. and 2002 Supplement. Salt Lake City: UT. 2002. Available online at http://envisionutah.net/ tools/urban-planning-tools-for-quality-grown

European Environment Agency. 1993. www.fao.org (accessed January 23, 2003).

Fisheries and Oceans Canada. "Definition of a Watershed." 2003.

Food and Agriculture Organization of the United Nations. "World Food Summit: Five Years Later." June 2002. www.fao.org/ WorldFoodSummit/sideevents/ papers/Y6899E.htm

Fort Worth. "What is Public Health." April 11, 2003. www.fortworthgov.org

Freeman, Lance, and Eliot Allen. "Developing the 'Broadway Corridor': San Antonio, Texas, Uses GIS Tool for Collaborative Planning." *ArcNews Online*. Winter 2001–2002. www.esri.com/news/arcnews/ winter0102articles/sanantonio-tx.html

Friedman, Abby. "Florida Counties Recognized for Unique Partnership." National Association of Counties. *County Services News*, August 12, 1996. www.naco.org

Fulton, William, Rolf Pendall, Mai Nguyen, and Alicia Harrison. "Who Sprawls Most? How Growth Patterns Differ Across the U.S." Brookings Institution, Center on Urban and Metropolitan Policy, July 2001. www.brookings.edu

Georgia Department of Community Affairs. www.dca.state.ga.us (accessed October 16, 2003).

Gratz, Roberta Brandes. "The Enduring Power of the Old Urbanism." *Metropolis Magazine*. February 2002. www.metropolismag.com

GreenInfrastructure.Net. "Definition." 2002a. http://www.greeninfrastructure.net/

GreenInfrastructure.Net. "The Importance of Green Infrastructure in Reducing Land Consumption." 2002b. www.greeninfrastructure.net

Green Map System. www.greenmap.com

Greenpeace. "Climate Time Bomb Catalogue." 1994 update. www.greenpeace.org

Green Space Design. "Green Space Design Process." www.greenspacedesign.org/home.html

Gunnett, Nigel, Carys Swanwick, and Helen Woolley. "Improving Urban Parks, Play Areas, and Green Spaces." May 2002. www.renewal.net

Guru, Manjula, and James Horne. "The Ogallala Aquifer." Kerr Center for Sustainable Agriculture. www.kerrcenter.com (accessed January 24, 2003).

Hamilton-Baillie, Ben. "Home Zones—Reconciling People, Places and Transport: A Study Tour of Denmark, Germany, Sweden and The Netherlands. 2001. Harvard Design School. www.gsd.harvard.edu

Harrison, Paul, and Fred Pearce. *AAAS Atlas of Population and Environment*. 2000. American Association for the Advancement of Science. http://atlas.aaas.org/

Heimlich, Ralph E., and William D. Anderson. "Development at the Urban Fringe and Beyond." U.S. Department of Agriculture, Economic Research Service, AER-803. June 2001. http://www.ers.usda.gov/publications/aer-agricultural-economic-report/aer803.aspx

High Plains Underground Water Conservation District No. 1. "The Ogallala Aquifer." 2002. www.hpwd.com (accessed January 24, 2003).

Home Zone News. "What Are Home Zones?" www.homezonenews.org.uk

National Invasive Species Information Center. USDA. Updated July 29, 2003. www.invasivespecies.gov

JaxPride. "Neighborhood Inventory of Visual Pollution." www.jaxpride.org

Johns Hopkins University, Applied Physics Laboratory Ocean Remote Sensing Group. "Color Landform Atlas of the United States." fermi.jhuapl.edu/states/states.html (accessed January 24, 2003).

Land Trust Alliance. "Referenda Victories Focus National Attention on Public Support for Open Space Protection." www.landtrustalliance.org/events-news

The Library of Congress. "City Life in the Late 19th Century." Modified September 26, 2002. www.loc.gov/teachers

Local Government Commission, Center for Livable Communities. www.lgc.org

Loudoun County Board of Supervisors. "Loudoun County's General Plan, 2001." loudoun.gov

Loudoun County, Virginia. "The Revised Comprehensive Plan." loudoun.gov

Loudoun County, Virginia, Department of Economic Development. "2001 Annual Growth Summary." May 2002. loudoun.gov (accessed January 24, 2003).

Lyman, Francesca. "The Geography of Health." October 30, 2002. Trust for Public Land. www.tpl.org

Majors-Duff, Lisa. "Greenways Specialist Explains Benefits of 'Green' Development." July 27, 2000. *The Sylva Herald and Ruralite*. www.thesylvaherald.com

MapQuest. http://mapquest.com

MapServer. www.mapserver.maptech.com (accessed November 22, 2002).

Maryland Department of Natural Resources. "Maryland Greenways Program." http://www.dnr.state.md.us/greenways/introduction.html

Maryland Department of Natural Resources. "Maryland's GreenPrint Program: Summary of Methods to Identify and Evaluate Maryland's Green Infrastructure." Draft, State of Maryland, Spring 2001. Available online at http://dnrweb.dnr.state.md.us/download/grantsandloans/gpevaluation.pdf

Mullahey, Ramona. "Using the Landscape of Place for Local Empowerment." *ResouccesZine*, Spring 1998. Available online from the American Planning Association at www.planning.org (accessed January 16, 2003).

National Arbor Day Foundation. Take Action; Plant a Tree Today For All the World to Share. www.arborday.org/arborday

National Park Service. "America's History Matters." National Park Service Press Release, August 29, 2000. www.nps.gov/news/release.htm?id=67

Orton Family Foundation. "Community Mapping Resources: Online Maps and Mapping Tools."

Parks and People. www.parksandpeople.org

PlanetWire.org. "Key Issues at WSSD: Food and Water." August 15, 2002. www.planetwire.org/details/3115

Population Reference Bureau. "QuickFacts." www.prb.org (accessed December 21, 2002).

Population Reference Bureau. "DataFinder: India and United States Population, Mid-2002." www.worldpop.org/datafinder.htm

Population Reference Bureau. "2004 World Population Data Sheet." Washington, DC: Population Reference Bureau, 2004. www.prb.org

Project for Public Spaces Inc. "Image of Bleecker St., New York City, 1999." 2003. http://pps.org/imagedb/image?image_id=13023&n_per_page=12&order_by=titl

Preservation Alliance of Virginia. "Legislative and Local Issues." 2003. http://preservationvirginia.org

Rails-to-Trails Conservancy. www.railtrails.org

The Road Information Program (TRIP). "Time Spent Stuck in Traffic Congestions Increased by Nearly 50 Percent During the 1990s." September 1, 2000. www.tripnet.org (accessed January 24, 2003).

The Dudley Street Neighborhood Initiative. "Quarterly Report." Winter-Spring 2004. www.dsni.org (accessed March 6, 2006).

Romanek, Andrew. "Impact of Senate Bill 1 on the Depletion of the Ogallala Aquifer." University of Texas at Austin. December 4, 1997. www.ce.utexas.edu/prof/maidment/grad/romanek/wtrproject/report.htm

Ruesink, Lou Ellen, ed. "Districts Make a Difference." Modified May 27, 1998. Texas Water Resources Institute. vol. 4, no. 8 (October 1978). http://twri.tamu.edu (accessed December 3, 2002).

Santoriello, Andrea, and Walter Block. "Externalities and the Environment." Libertyhaven. November 1996. www.liberty-haven.com (accessed December 11, 2002).

Scenic America. "Billboard Control: Fighting Visual Pollution." 2000a. www.scenic.org

Scenic America. "Community Choices for a More Scenic America." 2000b. www.scenicflorida.org

Sierra Club. "Stop Sprawl: Sprawl Overview." www.sierraclub.org/sprawl/factsheet.asp

Smart Growth Network. "About Smart Growth." www.smartgrowth.org

Smith, Dan. "The Case for Greener Cities." *American Forests Magazine*. Autumn 1999. www.oakvillegreen.com (accessed August 8, 2000).

Smith, Mark K. "Social Capital." Modified November 5, 2002. Infed.org. www.infed.org/biblio/social_capital.htm

TerraServer.com. http://terraserver.com

Texas Transportation Institute. "2004 Urban Mobility Study—Congestion Data for Your City." http://mobility.tamu.edu/ums

United Nations Population Fund. "Water, a Critical Resource." August 2002. www.unfpa.org (accessed July 23, 2003).

Urban Resources Initiative. "Community Greenspace Programs." http://environment.yale.edu/uri/#greenspace

U.S. Census Bureau. "Urban and Rural Population by State: 2000." 2000. www.census.gov/prod/2004pubs/03statab/pop.pdf

U.S. Census Bureau. "Loudoun County Department of Economic Development, and Loudoun County Fiscal Impact Committee." 2004. www.loudoun.gov/business

U.S. Census Bureau. "Resident Population Projections." 2004. www.census.gov/prod/2004pubs/03statab/pop.pdf

U.S. Census Bureau. "Introduction to Census 2000 Data Products." June 2001a. www.census.gov/prod/2001pubs/mso-01icdp.pdf

U.S. Census Bureau. "Summary of Travel Trends: 1977–2001." 2001b. www.census.gov/prod/2004pubs/03statab/trans.pdf

U.S. Census Bureau. "National Population Projections." Modified August 2, 2002. https://www.census.gov/geo/reference/urban-rural.html

U.S. Census Bureau. 2003a "Population: 1790-1990." www.census.gov

U.S. Census Bureau. "Population: 1960–2002." 2003b. U.S. Census Bureau. www.census.gov

U.S. Census Bureau. "Projected Population of the United States, by Race and Hispanic Origin: 2000–2050." 2004. http://www.census.gov/population/projections/

U.S. Census Bureau. " Population, Housing Units, Area Measurements, and Density: 1790 to 1990." 2005. www.census.gov/population/censusdata/table-2.pdf

U.S. Department of Agriculture, Farm Service Agency. "Fact Sheet Conservation Reserve Program." April 2003. https://www.fsa.usda.gov/Internet/FSA_File/crpfactsheet0213.pdf

U.S. Department of Housing and Urban Development. "Affordable Housing." http://portal.hud.gov/hudportal/HUD?src=/program_offices/comm_planning/affordablehousing

U.S. Department of Energy. "Ground Water." www.pantex.com (accessed December 3, 2002).

U.S. Environmental Protection Agency. "What on Earth Do You Know About Water?" www.epa.gov/gmpo/edresources/water_5.html

U.S. Environmental Protection Agency. "About Brownfields." 2004. http://www.epa.gov/brownfields/

U.S. Environmental Protection Agency. "Classifications of 1-Hour Ozone Nonattainment." 2004. www.epa.gov/oar/oaqps/greenbk/onc.html

U.S. Environmental Protection Agency. "About Smart Growth." www.epa.gov/livability/about_sg.htm

U.S. Geological Survey. "United States Energy and World Energy Production and Consumption Statistics." 1998. http://energy.usgs.gov/

U.S. Geological Survey. "Digital Backyard." usgs.gov (accessed October 27, 2002).

University of Illinois, Landscape and Human Health Laboratory. http://lhhl.illinois.edu/

University of Kansas. "Geologists Project Life of Ogallala Aquifer." July 12, 2001. http://archive.news.ku.edu/2001/01N/JulyNews/July12/aquifer.html

Wackernagel, Mathis, Larry Onisto, Alejandro Callejas Linares, Ina Susana López Falfán, Jesus Méndez García, Ana Isabel Suárez Guerrero, and Ma. Guadalupe Suárez Guerrero. "Ecological Footprints of Nations." March 10, 1997. Earth Council/Consejo de la Tierra. www.ucl.ac.uk/dpu-projects/drivers_urb_change/urb_environment/pdf_Sustainability/CSS_Wackernagel_footprints.pdf

Wall, Roland. "Current Issues Affecting World Water Supply." Academy of Natural Sciences. www.acnatsci.org

Washington Metropolitan Area Transit Authority. "Map of the Dupont Circle Station." www.stationmasters.com/System_Map/DUPONTCI/dupontci.html

Washington Metropolitan Area Transit Authority. "Making the Case for Transit: WMATA Regional Benefits of Transit" *www.wmata.com*

World Bank. "Water Supply and Sanitation." *www.worldbank.org/watsan*

World Resources Institute. "World Resources 2000–2001." *www.wri.org*

Xu, Yan. "Sense of Place and Identity." East St. Louis Action Research Project, University of Illinois at Urbana-Champaign. *www.eslarp. uiuc.edu/la/LA437-F95/reports/ yards/main.html*

[F] Videos

Sale, Kirkpatrick, John Todd, Nancy Jack Todd, Paul Winter, and Jeff Bercuvitz. *A Sense of Place*. Foundation for Global Community. (For more information, see *www.globalcommunity.org*.)

Cadillac Desert—Water and the Transformation of Nature. Public Broadcasting System. Boxed Set. 1996.

Making Sense of Place—Phoenix_The Urban Desert. Lincoln Institute of Land Policy. 2003.

Maps, Data, and Where to Find Information for Your Community

City and town governments are a primary source of pertinent community information, including comprehensive growth studies, zoning regulations, site plans, and subdivision ordinances (with addenda such as landscape ordinances, zoning maps, tax and topographic maps, planimetrics, sewer and water service maps, master street and highway maps, and bikeway maps). Those maps can usually be found in the local offices of planning or engineering services. Depending on your situation, you might want to track down the materials ahead of time for your students or encourage them to conduct research on their own. *Note*: The student pages also include tips on locating resources.

Two of the most useful resources to lend a new perspective about your community are planimetric maps and aerial photographs. ***Planimetric maps*** (or just "planimetrics") are maps that show line drawings of ground features. A planimetric map might show building outlines, edges of roadways, sidewalks, tree lines, bodies of water, manhole covers, and fire hydrants, and similar objects. A planimetric

map does not usually contain elevation data. (***Topographic maps***, however, are designed to show elevation, and they contain a system of lines to illustrate the "lay of the land." Topographic maps can be an important source of information but may be a bit cluttered for use in some activities.) Comparing planimetric maps can be one of the best ways to track changes in your community over time. Planimetric maps are usually at a scale of 1 inch to 100 feet and can be obtained in the survey and mapping department of a municipality or at the city or county engineer's office.

Aerial photographs (bird's-eye view) are excellent tools to show your students the elements of their community. Unlike other maps that highlight a theme (such as a road map) or that de-emphasize or exclude other components of your community, an aerial photograph offers an unbiased snapshot. If available from different time periods, aerial photographs also offer an excellent opportunity to track community change over time. An aerial photograph will not, however, reveal hidden elements (such as sewer lines) or artificial distinctions (such as zoning areas).

The U.S. Geological Survey (USGS) creates aerial photographs and topographic maps. You can obtain USGS images of your area through the

USGS for a fee (www.usgs.gov). Or you can find free aerial photographs of your area through:
- MapQuest (http://mapquest.com),
- TerraServer (http://terraserver.com and search for USGS maps),
- MapServer (www.mapserver.maptech.com).

Other possible sources of aerial photos for your area are the municipal offices, the local branch of the Natural Resources Conservation Services (formerly the Soil Conservation Service), and the state highway department. (*Note*: You may come across "digital aerial orthophotographs," which are essentially aerial photographs that have been processed to remove distortion.)

Regional planning agencies can be excellent sources of demographic information, with resources such as books, maps, and aerial photographs. Sometimes called planning district commissions, they typically provide a wealth of data on economic growth trends, as well as forecasts and inventories of human service resources. They provide information relevant to transportation and to physical and environmental planning. Planning district commissions typically publish studies on a variety of topics, such as watershed analysis, solid waste disposal, water quality, and scenic and open space. The regional information may also be compared to national trends, thereby providing a valuable context.

For a list of web links to other sites where you can find all kinds of free online maps of the United States, visit the following:
- http://geography.about.com. In addition to maps, the site also has links to other geography and data resources.
- http://fermi.jhuapl.edu/states/states.html. You will find the Color Landform Atlas of the United States. Click on your state and, for no fee, see shaded relief maps, satellite images, county maps, and maps from 1895.
- www.orton.org. The Orton Family Foundation website houses a great collection of community mapping resources, including online maps and mapping tools.

- www.census.gov. The U.S. Census Bureau provides a vast amount of population, housing, economic, and geographic data about our communities. Click on American Fact Finder (an online mapping resource on the site) to find ready-made ***thematic maps*** showing characteristics of your community. All you need to do is type in your school's or your community's address. Hundreds of maps are available that illustrate a variety of social and economic factors. For example, you might select a map showing average family size, mean travel time spent commuting to work, or mean age of community residents.
- http://earth.google.com/ Google Earth combines satellite imagery, maps, and point and zoom powers to explore anyplace on the planet. You can zoom in on your school address or a local greenspace area. Google Earth is free for personal use and no registration is required.

Concepts and Legislation

Smart Growth

The term "smart growth" was coined to describe development that serves the community, the economy, and the environment. It provides a framework for communities to make informed decisions about how and where they grow. Smart growth espouses a number of principles to guide development. For example, smart growth proponents encourage the creation of compact, **mixed-use neighborhoods**. Today, some communities are creating compact neighborhoods that use land more efficiently and that include bicycle facilities, common areas, convenient access to transit, front yards designed to encourage socializing, and pedestrian crossings.

"Mixed use" is also an important principle in new community design. In mixed-use developments, land uses with complementary functions are located close together. Complementary uses may include housing, movie theaters, offices, restaurants, schools, and shopping—destinations people travel to on a regular basis. A mix of land uses can minimize travel distances and improve access to education, employment, recreational opportunities, or services. Locating activities closer together allows trips to be made by walking or bicycling rather than by driving motor vehicles, thus offering both health and environmental benefits.

Zoning

Though zoning is often blamed for sprawl and poorly planned growth, when properly applied, it can actually result in aesthetically pleasing, efficient, and livable communities. One example is Seaside, Florida.

The town of Seaside is the result of five years of research and development by Andres Duany and Elizabeth Plater-Zyberk. Duany and Plater-Zyberk traveled from Key West to New Orleans while studying styles found in small Southern towns. Their research led to a comprehensive plan that proposed 350 residences, 100 to 200 lodging units, a downtown retail center, and a civic conference center. Furthermore, all buildings were modeled after regional examples, thus maintaining the richness and character of a small town. However, Seaside departed from surrounding communities because it incorporated the automobile.

Individual sections within the community were zoned by type of architectural style rather than by the traditional zoning that is based on function. The town is divided into eight sections, each with a different architectural style endemic to the southeastern United States. Each section also includes different occupancies, such as strictly residential, residential and lodging, residential and retail, or residential and light industrial. This mix establishes cohesiveness in each distinct neighborhood. However, when taken as a whole, a diversified and architecturally rich town emerges.

The town established a balance between allowing architectural freedom yet maintaining cohesion. For instance, compulsory rules maintain that all public buildings must be white, yet style and design is left for the developer to decide. Also, all buildings must pass through a review process before construction can begin. Every year, the town hires a different architect, thus ensuring variety within the established regulations.

Some unforeseen consequences resulted from the praise the community has received. Land prices in Seaside have soared higher than in bordering communities, which has made it impossible for lower-income families to purchase land or to rent lodging.

Legislation

Numerous pieces of legislation have influenced smart growth. Following is a list of the most influential government measures:

Housing Act of 1937—Federal money could be used to build a new housing complex whenever one was torn down. The goal was to improve slums by replacing old housing with new.

Housing Act of 1949—Using federal funds, authorities could seize entire blocks of slum housing and could sell the land for redevelopment. However, new housing wasn't always constructed; many blocks became parking lots. This legislation also led to the decline of inner cities as businesses were forced out to make room for a redevelopment that never occurred.

Federal-Aid to Highway/Interstate Highway Act (1956)—The rise in popularity of the automobile after World War II meant that the expressway system needed to be expanded into cities. This expansion proved difficult and, greatly affected neighborhoods and commercial developments. Building a system of highways led to a significant change in the appearance and layout of cities across the country.

Urban Mass Transit Act (1964)—This legislation authorized federal grants to finance up to two-thirds of the cost of new mass transit facilities. In all, $375 million over three years was allotted.

Highway Beautification Act (1965)—Section 4(f) of this act prohibited any federally funded highways to be constructed in parks, wildlife refuges, and historic areas unless there was no alternative.

Federal Highway Act (1970)—This legislation required states to consult with local officials on urban highway projects in order to give more attention to social, economic, and environmental impacts of construction. This change occurred after passage of the National Environmental Policy Act, which required an environmental impact statement to be filed for all federally funded actions, including highway construction.

Urban Mass Transit Assistance Act (1970)—This act established a long-term federal commitment to mass transit with funding obligations. It also allocated $3 billion for a five-year period.

Federal Highway Act (1973)—The act focused on mass transit, replacing the old emphasis on interstate highway projects. It also provided an 80 percent federal match to state or local funds. Money came from the country's general fund instead of the Highway Trust Fund. However, after the gas tax was raised under the Surface Transportation Act of 1974, the Mass Transit Account was created to help fund mass transportation.

Intermodal Surface Transportation Enhancement Act (ISTEA)—Passage of this act changed the way government funding was used. Previously, funding could be used only for projects for which the government had designated the funds. With ISTEA, this money became flexible, allowing states to use funds on any transportation project (e.g., bike paths, mass transit, roads).

Equity Act for the 21st Century (TEA-21)—Formerly the ISTEA, this legislation provided $216 billion in funding through 2003 with $41 billion for transit.

Sources:
Friedman 2002 (A).
Gillham 2002 (A).
Smart Growth Network/ICMA 2002 (C).

What Makes Up an Environmental Issue?

Environmental issues occur because people have differing views on the environment. If everyone had the same viewpoint, there would be no controversy—and no issue. It is easier to understand an environmental issue and to make sound decisions when all the information, scientific facts, and data are known about the subject. In the real world, however, there are always unknowns.

Components of an Environmental Issue

To assume an educated position about an environmental issue, we are obligated to consider various components and their definitions.

Problem is a condition in which something is at risk. Environmental problems involve the interaction of humans and the environment, and the threat or risk associated with that involvement.

Issue is a problem—or its solution—for which differing beliefs and values exist, usually involving two or more parties who don't agree. If students don't understand varying beliefs and values of the disagreeing parties, they won't understand the concept of an environmental issue.

Values as a term means the relative worth an individual places on something. Some examples used in labeling environmental values are as follows:
* *Aesthetic* refers to an appreciation of beauty through the senses.
* *Cultural* refers to the maintenance of the integrity of natural systems.
* *Economic* refers to the exchange of goods and services for money.
* *Educational* refers to the benefits derived from learning or instruction.

* *Egocentric* refers to a focus on self-satisfaction and personal fulfillment.
* *Legal* refers to the law and its enforcement.
* *Recreational* refers to the use of leisure time.
* *Social* refers to shared human empathy, feelings, and status, or to an interaction of the human condition.

Players and Positions are terms for the individuals, groups, or both that are involved in an issue, plus where they stand on the issue.

Beliefs is a term for the ideas concerning the issue, whether true or not, held by the players. A belief is strongly tied to a person's values.

Solutions as a term means the various strategies proposed to resolve the issue.

What Makes Up an Acceptable Solution? The following criteria should be met when reading an acceptable solution:
* The public is involved in the decision-making process.
* The interested public sectors reach a compromise.
* The compromise meets objectives for managing the resource.
* The compromise conforms to law.

Teaching Controversial Issues

Many teachers steer clear of controversy in the classroom and, therefore, do not discuss environmental issues, which can be controversial, with their students. Yet, controversy can provide opportunities for increasing the quality of students' thinking and their ability to solve problems.

Although controversy is often uncomfortable, it also tends to be intellectually stimulating. As long as students clearly understand that some issues are controversial precisely because they are too complex to have clear-cut "right" and "wrong" solutions, the students can focus on the process of clarifying their own viewpoints through debate and reflection.

Jean Piaget, Lawrence Kohlberg, and other learning theorists address the importance of cognitive disequilibration in intellectual and moral development. Students benefit from opportunities to consider other viewpoints and to defend their own. Productive conflict appears to promote the development of cognitive and moral reasoning; it thus has a valid place in a learning environment.

The Role of the Teacher

Teaching about an environmental issue in the classroom may require a shift in your role as teacher. The teacher operates more like a conductor orchestrating opportunities for students to think about complex issues in a safe, supportive atmosphere, rather than as the traditional instructor who is focused primarily on teaching information to be learned. Teachers need to allow ideas to develop, understanding to deepen, and judgments to be made and tested.

Teachers can support student learning by encouraging and facilitating discussion, by providing accurate factual information, and by allowing sufficient time to study a multifaceted environmental issue.

Instructional Strategies

Activities should emphasize strategies that minimize polarization of viewpoints and that maximize quantity and quality of ideas. Through frequent class discussions and cooperative learning experiences, students should examine their thoughts and opinions without pressure to come to the "right" conclusion. Emphasis is on the process of sharing opinions, acquiring and judging new information, and making and reflecting on those decisions. The following suggestions support a classroom climate that allows this kind of thinking and learning to take place:

1. Establish clear rules for behavior during class discussions. Those rules should first and foremost preserve the integrity of the individual. Personal attacks and name calling should be forbidden, and students should be reminded that any conflicts that arise must be conflicts of ideas, not people. Conflicts of ideas can be positive; exploring conflicting ideas is a way to advance one's thinking.

2. Pay attention and respond to feelings underlying expressed ideas. Sometimes students are afraid to voice personal beliefs and convictions; they need to be reassured that this expression is okay.

3. When a conflict arises, observe the group, describe what you observe, and provide time for students to describe what they observe and feel. Engage students in conflict resolution techniques such as reversing roles in arguments or negotiating a win–win resolution (so everyone wins in some way). Provide support for students who are anxious throughout the conflict; many people are uncomfortable with disagreement.

4. Use questioning strategies to clarify and advance students' thinking. Ask students to restate an idea in another way, to elaborate, or to reiterate what they hear so they can confirm or clarify. Questions can also be used to advance thinking. Ask students to apply an idea to a real or hypothetical situation, to consider discrepancies in their thinking, or to reassess their idea in light of new information.

5. Take time after each class discussion to analyze your students' and your own thinking so that you value the evolution of thinking rather than simply the views expressed. By identifying individual biases, defense strategies, and styles of argumentation, a group can operate more consciously as it tries to fully understand a controversial issue.

Working with Parents and Administrators

A primary reason that many teachers avoid teaching about controversial issues is fear of resistance from parents and administrators. The following suggestions will help you avoid resistance and gain administrators' and parents' support.

1. Examine community attitudes about environmental issues in local newspapers, and listen to public discourse about those problems. This background will help you anticipate potential concerns and choose how and when to teach a particular environmental issue.

2. Consider the occupations of parents in the community. Will any of them be particularly sensitive to certain environmental issues? If so, think through how to best work with those parents so they do not feel threatened by your lesson unit.

3. Determine whether or not any lesson or part of a lesson will raise concern among parents or administrators and then modify the lesson accordingly.

4. Choose a method to inform, first, administrators and, second, parents, of your plan. Also choose a method to gather their input. Include examples of lessons. Emphasize that the teacher's role is to facilitate discussion and to help students find out how to think about an issue—not what to think.

5. Provide plenty of time for feedback from administrators and parents. Incorporate their ideas in ways that make the lessons more instructionally sound.

6. As you teach the lessons, keep parents and administrators informed. Describe for them the students' activities and your observations as your students learn about an environmental issue.

7. After you have taught the lessons, provide administrators with a concise assessment of student learning. Describe ways that you would modify the lessons in the future.

Successful Cooperative Learning

Cooperative learning is an instructional method in which students work together in small groups to achieve common goals. The method can encourage cooperation and communication skills and can be a valuable addition to your instructional repertoire.

Used appropriately, cooperative learning can help motivate students, promote active learning, foster respect, improve language skills, and increase teacher effectiveness. The essential feature of cooperative learning is that the success of one student helps other students to be successful. The process helps promote equality of all students by encouraging them to cooperate with each other to complete projects.

Steps

To foster success among your students, use the following steps as a guide:

1. Form cooperative groups. Carefully select members for each group. Mix students' academic and social abilities, gender, cultural backgrounds, handicaps, and interests for each group.

2. Assign roles. Students are more likely to work together if each one has a job that contributes to the task. Roles need to be taught and modeled to students, then practiced. Depending on the activity, you may assign students any of the following roles:
• *Recorder*, who writes the group's answers
• *Reporter*, who reports the group's answer to the entire class
• *Manager*, who gathers and returns materials used by the group
• *Facilitator*, who organizes the group's work, makes sure the group understands its job, and takes the group's questions to the teacher after trying to get the answers from the group
• *Reader*, who reads the directions of other materials out loud to the group in such a way that team members can understand the directions
• *Artist*, who draws illustrations or diagrams for the group
• *Researcher*, who looks up unknown words in the dictionary or encyclopedia.

3. Develop and post the classroom rules. Review the rules and explain them with examples of effective behavior (e.g., what is good listening?). Set expectations for effective group behavior. Examples include these:
• Everyone participates and helps others.
• Everyone listens to others.
• Each student uses a quiet voice.
• Each student does the task assigned.

4. Arrange groups in small clusters. Arrange desks and chairs to allow students within the group to see and hear each other as they work together.

5. Encourage students to practice positive social skills. Students must be taught to practice the social skills necessary for effective cooperative work. Those skills involve sharing, compromising, listening, taking turns, helping each other, praising, providing positive feedback, accepting individual differences, and disagreeing respectfully. Students must develop the feeling that they are responsible for and accountable to the group for doing their best. They need the opportunity to help each other, which you can encourage by having them establish mutual goals and joint rewards and then share materials and information.

6. State directions clearly, and model appropriate procedures. Clearly state the task and the time allotted. Check for understanding. Describe the criteria that would signify the group was successful. Remind students of the specific behaviors expected, such as everyone's participating.

7. Monitor groups. Teach students the skills you see them lacking. Turn problems back to the group to solve as you act as a facilitator or

consultant. Practice is the key to the successful use of cooperative learning. When necessary, encourage students to solve problems or to teach skills to one another.

8. Evaluate outcomes and debrief after each lesson. During debriefing, evaluate how effectively students are using their social skills when working together and how they could use them more effectively next time. This feedback is essential to improving groups that are not working effectively together and to rewarding those groups that are. Use the following questions to help students focus on their experiences:
• Did everyone in your group participate?
• How could you encourage someone to participate?
• How did you help your group during the activity?
• What would you do to make your group work together better?

On the following page is a group evaluation form. Pass it out to the students, and use the results to help determine students' grades.

Group Evaluation Form

Name: _____

Directions: Write the name of each group member, including yourself, on the lines below. Then, on a scale of 1 (Poor) to 5 (Excellent), please rate the participation and contributions of each member in your group, including yourself. This evaluation, along with the evaluations of other group members, will help determine the individual grade for each person in the group.

	Poor		Average		Excellent

1. The level of participation of each group member was

   a. _____ 1 2 3 4 5
   b. _____ 1 2 3 4 5
   c. _____ 1 2 3 4 5
   d. _____ 1 2 3 4 5
   e. _____ 1 2 3 4 5

2. The quality of work contributed by each group member was

   a. _____ 1 2 3 4 5
   b. _____ 1 2 3 4 5
   c. _____ 1 2 3 4 5
   d. _____ 1 2 3 4 5
   e. _____ 1 2 3 4 5

3. The level of respect and cooperation shown by each group member was

   a. _____ 1 2 3 4 5
   b. _____ 1 2 3 4 5
   c. _____ 1 2 3 4 5
   d. _____ 1 2 3 4 5
   e. _____ 1 2 3 4 5

4. Please list the role(s) of each group member, including yourself:

5. Comments:

Correlation to National Science Education Standards
Grades 9-12, National Academy of Sciences

STANDARD	ACTIVITY 1 Personal Places	ACTIVITY 2 Community Character	ACTIVITY 3 Mapping Your Community Through Time	ACTIVITY 4 Neighborhood Design	ACTIVITY 5 Green Space	ACTIVITY 6 A Vision for the Future	ACTIVITY 7 Far-Reaching Decisions	ACTIVITY 8 Regional Community Issues: The Ogallala Aquifer
Science as Inquiry		X	X	X			X	X
Physical Science								
Life Science				X	X	X		
Earth and Space Science					X	X		
Science and Technology		X	X			X		
Science in Personal and Social Perspectives	X	X	X	X	X	X	X	X
History and Nature of Science	X				X	X		

Correlation to Curriculum Standards for Social Studies Grades 9-12, National Council for the Social Studies

STANDARD*	ACTIVITY 1 Personal Places	ACTIVITY 2 Community Character	ACTIVITY 3 Mapping Your Community Through Time	ACTIVITY 4 Neighborhood Design	ACTIVITY 5 Green Space	ACTIVITY 6 A Vision for the Future	ACTIVITY 7 Far-Reaching Decisions	ACTIVITY 8 Regional Community Issues: The Ogallala Aquifer
Culture	a b	c d					h	
Time, Continuity, Change		b c	b c d e f	d	f	f	f	e f
People, Places, Environments	a b c g	b c g	a b c d g h i	b c d g k	b c d e h k	b c d e h k	b c d	b c e j f g
Individual Development & Identity	a b c	a	b c			a	a	b
Individuals, Groups & Institutions	b	e h						
Power, Authority & Governance			b				a	c
Production, Distribution & Consumption						a b	a f	b c d j
Science, Technology & Society			a b			d	f	
Global Connections							d h	
Civic Ideals & Practices					e j	i j	e	c d f

*Letters refer to Performance Expectations in the Curriculum Standards for Social Studies.

Conceptual Framework

Theme: Diversity

1.0 Throughout the world, there is a great diversity of habitats, organisms, societies, technologies, and cultures.

Diversity in Environments

1.1 Biodiversity results from the interaction of living and nonliving environmental components such as air, water, climate, and geologic features.

1.2 Forests, as well as other ecosystems, contain numerous habitats that support diverse populations of organisms.

1.3 The Earth's atmosphere, water, soil, climate, and geology vary from region to region, thus creating a wide diversity of biological communities.

Diversity of Resources and Technologies

1.4 Humans use tools and technologies to adapt and alter environments and resources to meet their physical, social, and cultural needs.

1.5 Technologies vary from simple hand tools to large-scale and complex machinery, mechanisms, and systems.

1.6 Successful technologies are those that are appropriate to the efficient and sustainable use of resources, and to the preservation and enhancement of environmental quality.

Diversity Among and Within Societies and Cultures

1.7 Human societies vary greatly and inhabit many land forms and climates throughout the world.

1.8 Humans throughout the world create differing social, cultural, and economic systems and organizations to help them meet their physical and spiritual needs.

1.9 The standard of living of various peoples throughout the world is dependent on environmental quality; the availability, utilization, and distribution of resources; the government; and culture of its inhabitants.

1.10 Natural beauty, as experienced in forests and other habitats, enhances the quality of human life by providing artistic and spiritual inspiration, as well as recreational and intellectual opportunities.

Theme: Interrelationships

2.0 The ecological, technological, and socio-cultural systems are interactive and interdependent.

Environmental Interrelationships

2.1 Organisms are interdependent, and depend on nonliving components of the Earth.

2.2 Altering the environment affects all life forms, including humans, and the interrelationships that link them.

2.3 Organisms adapt to changes in the environment according to the genetic and behavioral capacity of their species.

Resource and Technological Interrelationships

2.4 Resource management technologies interact and influence environmental quality; the acquisition, extraction, and transportation of natural resources; all life forms; and each other.

2.5 While technological advances decrease the incidence of disease and death, the ever-increasing world population is placing heavy demands on the finite resources of the Earth.

2.6 International cooperation directed toward conserving resources and protecting environmental quality is beneficial to human health and the well-being of other life forms.

2.7 By reducing waste and recycling materials, individuals and societies can extend the value and utility of resources and also promote environmental quality.

Societal and Cultural Interrelationships

2.8 Human societies and cultures throughout the world interact with each other and affect natural systems upon which they depend.

2.9 The quantity and quality of resources and their use—or misuse—by humans affect the standard of living of societies.

2.10 Cultural and societal perspectives influence the attitudes, beliefs, and biases of people toward the use of resources and environmental protection.

2.11 All humans consume products and thereby affect the availability of renewable and nonrenewable natural resources.

2.12 The extracting, processing, transporting, and marketing of natural resources provide employment opportunities for many people.

Theme: Systems

3.0 Environmental, technological, and social systems are interconnected and interacting.

Environmental Systems

3.1 In biological systems, energy flows and materials continually cycle in predictable and measurable patterns.

3.2 Plant and animal populations exhibit interrelated cycles of growth and decline.

3.3 Pollutants are harmful by-products of human and natural systems which can enter ecosystems in various ways.

3.4 Ecosystems possess measurable indicators of environmental health.

Resource Management and Technological Systems

3.5 The application of scientific knowledge and technological systems can have positive or negative effects on the environment.

3.6 Resource management and technological systems can help societies meet, within limits, the needs of a growing human population.

3.7 Conservation technology enables humans to maintain and extend the productivity of vital resources.

Systems in Societies and Cultures

3.8 Most cultures have beliefs, values, and traditions that shape human interactions with the environment and its resources.

3.9 In democratic societies, citizens have a voice in shaping resource and environmental management policies. They also share in the responsibility of conserving resources and behaving in an environmentally responsible manner.

3.10 In democratic societies, individuals and groups, working through governmental

channels, can influence the way public and private lands and resources are managed.

3.11 Effective citizen involvement in the environmental decision-making process involves a careful study of all sides of the issues, along with the ability to differentiate between honest, factually accurate information and propaganda.

Theme: Structure and Scale

4.0 Technologies, societal institutions, and components of natural and human-built environments vary in structure and scale.

Structures and Scale in Environments

4.1 Populations of organisms exhibit variations in size and structure as a result of their adaptation to their habitats.

4.2 The structure and scale of an ecosystem are influenced by factors such as soil type, climate, availability of water, and human activities.

4.3 When the Earth is studied as an interacting ecological system, every action, regardless of its scale, affects the biosphere in some way.

Structure and Scale in Resources and Technologies

4.4 Technologies vary in size, structure, and complexity and in their positive and negative effects on the environment.

4.5 Conservation and management technologies, when appropriately applied to the use or preservation of natural resources, can enhance and extend the usefulness of the resource, as well as the quality of the environment.

4.6 Human-built environments, if planned, constructed, and landscaped to be compatible with the environment in which they will be located, can conserve resources, enhance environmental quality, and promote the comfort and well-being of those who will live within them.

4.7 International cooperation on resource management and environmental improvement programs can be beneficial to people in many parts of the world.

Structure and Scale in Societies and Cultures

4.8 The structure and scale of the natural resources in a given area shape the economy upon which the society and its culture is based. Cultural structures and actions affect the management of resources and environmental quality.

4.9 Governmental, social, and cultural structures and actions affect the management of resources and environmental quality.

4.10 Demographics influence environmental quality, government policy, and resource use.

Theme: Patterns of Change

5.0 Structure and systems change over various periods of time.

Patterns of Change in the Environment

5.1 Organisms change throughout their lifetimes. Species of organisms change over long periods of time.

5.2 Although species become extinct naturally, the increasing number of extinctions in recent history may be linked to the rapid increase in human population.

5.3 As organisms go through their life cycle of growth, maturity, decline, and death, their role in the ecosystem also changes.

5.4 Ecosystems change over time through patterns of growth and succession. They are also affected by other phenomena such as disease, insects, fire, weather, climate, and human intervention.

Patterns of Change in Resources and Technologies

5.5 Our increasing knowledge of the Earth's ecosystems influences strategies used for resource management and environmental stewardship.

5.6 Technologies that are developed to meet the needs of an increasing world population should also be environmentally sound.

5.7 To be most effective, new technologies require well-informed and highly skilled workers.

Patterns of Change in Societies and Cultures

5.8 Governments change and evolve over the years. Such changes affect the lives of its citizens, as well as resource management and environmental policies.

5.9 Consumers "drive" the marketplace with their demands for goods and services. Such demands shift with time and may have positive or negative effects on the resource base and environmental quality.

5.10 Industries usually respond to consumer demand for recyclable, recycled, or otherwise environmentally friendly products.

5.11 Leisure and recreational pursuits can have an impact on forests and other resource-producing areas.

5.12 Increased public knowledge of the environment and the need for conservation of natural resources have resulted in lifestyle changes in many cultures.

Notes